**Editor-In-Chief, Michael Spivak**

# science
## INTERNATIONAL

David Langer
Gail Macnaughton
Jill Macfarlane
Molly Connors
Matti Korhonen
Paula Quigley
Joanna Woloszczuk
Alexandra Anderson
Helen Wooldridge
Steven Smith

# What Will They Think of Next!

McClelland and Stewart

ISBN: 0-7710-8221-5

*The Canadian Publishers*
McClelland and Stewart Limited
25 Hollinger Road, Toronto

Printed and bound in Canada
by Webcom Limited

---

Canadian Cataloguing in Publication Data

Main entry under title:
What Will They Think of Next!

includes index.
ISBN 0-7710-8221-5 pa.

1. Science—Miscellanea.    I. Spivak, Michael

Q173.W48     502     C79-094407-3

---

The dreaded science-fiction ray gun that could zap your enemies is now a reality, and it's riding shotgun on your typewriter. Dr. Arthur Schalow, Professor of Physics at Stanford University, has developed a miniature laser gun so small that it can actually be attached to a typewriter. If further tests continue to be successful, secretaries around the world may have a new weapon in the continuing battle against typewriter errors. When a wrong letter is typed, a flash of light from the gun zaps a laser beam at the page, and the mistake is erased. The system works because of the high speed of the laser pulse. One-half of a millisecond of exposure is long enough to vaporize the carbon ink pigment on the surface of the paper. But, because the action is so quick, the paper itself remains completely unharmed. The wrong letter has disappeared into thin air and the paper is clean again, ready for the right letter to be typed in the same space.

Laser Eraser

When a person has to abandon a ship at sea, his chances of survival are minimized without fresh drinking water. But British engineers have developed a compact plastic device enabling people lost at sea to create their own supply of fresh water. Called the "solar still", it uses the heat of the sun to turn salt water into fresh water, keeping survivors alive until help arrives.

After the cone is inflated the survivor simply fills the base of the still with salt water using an attached tube. Inside there's a black material that absorbs the salt water like a towel. As the sun beats down on the material, water evaporates onto the plastic cone, leaving the salt trapped in the "towelling". The condensed water on the underside of the cone drips down and collects in a tube, which floats in the sea to keep the water cool. In a single day, up to three pints of pure, cool water can be collected—more than enough to keep the survivor alive until he can be rescued.

## Solar Still

# Amniotic-Sac Bandages

Scientists have recently discovered a miraculous new substance that can reduce pain, fight infection, and promote healing. This space-age medical discovery was not manufactured in a laboratory; it was found in a hospital garbage can.

The new substance is the thin, fragile membrane that covers the fetus during pregnancy. Called the "amniotic sac", the membrane is usually thrown away because the baby doesn't need it after birth. But doctors at St. Michael's Hospital in Toronto have discovered that the precious membrane can be used to help people who are suffering from burns and badly infected wounds. Placed directly on the wound itself, the amniotic sac seems to reduce pain. It fights dangerous infections, and it even helps to tell the doctor when the danger of infection has finally passed, because it drops off when the skin beneath has begun to heal.

# Jogging Jerseys

Dairy cows, it seems, are getting more and more like people every day. They're out of shape, with flabby muscles and too much fat.

One reason for this lack of physical fitness is that, under modern farming methods, cows no longer wander around a pasture. Instead, they're confined to a drylot where their needs are instantly provided for. All they have to do in this relaxing environment is lie down, get up, eat, be milked, and give birth to a calf once in awhile. The result of this soft living is poor health, lack of stamina, and a shorter life span.

In order to remedy the situation, the cows, just like people, have taken up jogging. But it's not easy to get a cow into sneakers and out on the track.

That's why agricultural researchers at Utah State University decided to give them a hand. Dairy scientist Dr. Robert Lamb has designed a mechanical exerciser for cows that forces them to walk at a good pace. The cow exerciser is a fenced ring with a motorized, moveable tailgate that gently pats the cows' behinds, making them move along.

Researchers discovered that cows who had taken up jogging gave birth more easily and even produced more milk while consuming less feed. The exerciser also healed sore hoofs, straightened out unsightly humped backs, and melted away excess fat.

**A**gricultural scientists are always searching for ways to put more food on the table. A few years ago, they thought they had come up with a brilliant idea. They knew that 25 per cent of the protein in a chicken is in the feathers. They dreamed of featherless chickens, which would require no plucking and provide more meat per pound at the very same price. After years of work the scientists were successful, and a chicken without feathers was finally hatched.

However, there were problems. Researchers found that their birds with bare bottoms were so cold that they kept running around, trying to keep warm.

In fact, all this activity made the chilly chickens so nervous that most of them became sick with stomach ulcers and wasted away.

After this fiasco, you'd think that scientists would have learned that it doesn't pay to fool with Mother Nature. But in yet another experiment at a research laboratory in Iowa, genetic engineers, attempting to satisfy drumstick lovers the world over, hatched a four-legged chicken. The only problem this time was that the chicken was so ugly that no one would eat it.

# Bare Bottom Broilers

# Electric Money

Not long ago, an armed bandit entered a Texas loan company, pointed his gun at one of the tellers, and handed her a note demanding money. The terrified teller stuffed a wad of bills into a large envelope and the robber escaped. With the stash tucked neatly inside his shirt, the bank robber thought he was safe – until the envelope suddenly exploded in a cloud of smoke, spewing out tear gas and red dye. Within minutes he was arrested, and later he confessed to the crime.

This confused and startled robber was the victim of a new device developed by crime researchers at the United States Currency Protection Corporation. Called the "currency guard", this remarkable electronic unit is hidden inside a banded bundle of money. Looking for all the world like a half-inch stack of five-dollar bills, the device is really a time bomb containing tear

gas, a red dye that can't be washed off, and a timing device triggered to go off a few minutes after the robber leaves the bank. The currency guard is activated by a coded radio signal that is continuously emitted at the doors of the bank.

In the event of a robbery, the teller just mixes a specially treated packet of bills with the other money. In a matter of minutes the unit goes off, shocking the robber and alerting passers-by.

Crime researchers are so confident that their system works that they've offered to reimburse a bank up to $5,000 if the cash is not recovered in thirty days.

# Instant Muscles

If you want to have large rippling biceps, a well developed chest, and stomach muscles like an iron wall, you may be interested in a fascinating new machine developed in the Soviet Union. The device builds instant muscles without sweat, weights, or exercise, and is remarkably simple to use. The machine is called a "muscle stimulator", and variations of it have been employed in physical therapy for years. To use it, you place electrodes on your muscles and turn on an electric current, which makes your muscles contract as the current flows. Completely painless, the stimulator is used for ten seconds at a time, followed by a rest of fifty seconds. If you use the machine every day for forty days, you can be sure of an increase in muscle strength by a full 50 per cent. The Russians have used the technique on Olympic sprinters, weight-lifters, and wrestlers, with excellent results. After nineteen days the spontaneous strength of the wrestlers, for example, was up by 50 per cent, and their jumping ability rose by 19 per cent. There seems to be only one catch: the mushrooming muscles aren't permanent. If treatment is stopped, muscle tone deteriorates, and within six months the user reverts to his former flabby self. But, say the Russians, all athletes who stop training lose muscle tone at much the same pace, so the problem is really a minor one. As long as Olympic competitors continue to use the jiffy muscle-making machine, it may well remain their very best friend.

The next time you have a tooth knocked out, just pick it up and pop it back into your mouth. Don't put it where the hole is: put it between the cheek and the gum.

This advice comes from one of the world's leading authorities on dental injuries, Dr. Jens Ove Andreasen of the University of Copenhagen. He says that teeth can be replanted easily, but sometimes the body rejects the lost

# Knocked Out Teeth

tooth because the delicate tissue that covers the roots has been damaged by handling or cleaning. So if you should lose a tooth, don't even try brushing off the dirt. Just put it in your mouth and let the saliva bathe and clean it naturally. A word of warning, however: once the tooth is safely in your mouth, you've only got about ninety minutes to get to a dentist, in order to have it replanted successfully.

# Beetle Bone-Cleaners

Museums often have large quantities of bones that need cleaning, bones that once could be cleaned only by hand – a long and extremely tedious process. Some chemicals, such as ammonia, do a whistle-clean job, but they also tend to dissolve the bones themselves.

Lately museum workers have been turning to a special group of helpers, unpaid assistants who never went to college and don't have any particular skills. They're little beetles called "dermestid", and they're just doing what comes naturally.

During the larval stage, the dermestid are particularly fond of chewing the meat off bones, and museum officials are only too happy to let them. While the beetles get a tasty meal, the museum gets a perfectly clean animal skeleton. After the beetles have done their job, the skeleton is placed under very bright lights, which flush out any larvae that might still be there. All the museum curator has to do is bleach the bones and dip them in a cleaning solution, and they're ready to be mounted and displayed.

The only problem is that the beetles also enjoy munching on stuffed animals and chomping through carpets – a performance that museum officials now discourage with fumigations twice a year, as well as with a new security system using sealed double doors, which help keep the beetles safely confined to their quarters.

On one of his many cross-country business flights, Dr. Richard W. Roberts, a research scientist with General Electric, was seated next to a blind traveller. When lunch was served, Dr. Roberts was amazed to see how well the man managed to eat on his own – until the stewardess came by to pour a cup of hot coffee.

Blind people are capable of taking care of themselves, but when it comes to hot liquids they sometimes have a lot of trouble. Normally, a blind person places his finger over the edge of the cup until he feels the warmth of the hot liquid. But this can be dangerous, particularly if he's pouring the hot liquid himself and it comes out too quickly.

This dilemma started Dr. Roberts thinking: why not develop a small, inexpensive device that can be slipped on any sort of pot or cup to alert the blind person instantly that the liquid is near the top?

Back in his laboratory, the scientist and his associate, George Jernakoff, developed a device that weighs only one and a half ounces and is about the size of a thumb. It hangs over the side of a cup, attached by two sensitive, L-shaped "feelers". When the cup is nearly full, the liquid completes an electric circuit between the two "feelers" and sets off a loud buzzer, warning the blind person to stop pouring.

Anything that helps a handicapped person to lead a more normal life is a welcome invention, and it's heartwarming to know that, for blind people, this tiny device that fits on the edge of a cup is helping to make that morning cup of coffee a relaxing pleasure instead of a potential danger.

15

**Hail Gun**

results are obtained when the interval between explosions is about fifteen seconds, producing a series of rising shock waves that actually change the physical structure of the cloud, so that rain falls to the ground instead of hail.

One of these units can protect between one hundred and two hundred acres of land, and a whole series of the hail converters could protect vast orchards, vineyards, and tobacco plantations from the seasonal onslaught of hail all over the country.

Although hail is usually just a mild inconvenience to most of us, for farmers it can sometimes mean the total destruction of their crops. French weather-researchers have discovered a new way to fight hail storms by using a gun. But the weapon doesn't fire bullets; it fires shock waves.

The gun is really an acetylene generator with a giant, horn-like funnel that points skyward. The acetylene gas is mixed with air in a combustion chamber, where the explosive mixture is ignited by an electric spark. The resulting explosion creates a violent shock wave that shoots up the funnel and into the cloud overhead. The best

Research engineers at Sandia Laboratories in Albuquerque, New Mexico, have developed a cannon that's being used to explore layers of soil and rock below the surface of the earth. Scientists can tell the difference between various layers by measuring the speed of a huge projectile as it shoots into the earth and gradually slows down.

The new earth gun is different from a conventional artillery piece, because the thirty-five-foot-long barrel is open at both ends. To load the gun, technicians place a huge mass of steel weighing over sixteen hundred pounds into the barrel.

The next step is to load the charge of explosive powder, which is sandwiched between the steel slug and the projectile. In most experimental tests, the projectile is five feet long and six inches wide and, with its outer protective wrap, it fits snugly into the barrel.

From a vertical position, the projectile penetrates 130 feet down into the ground, and it can be shot on an angle from as little as fifteen degrees away from the horizontal.

After the test firings are completed, a four-foot hole is drilled so that a miner can climb down and free the heavy projectile from the soil and rock.

Then slow-motion photography and sensitive measuring devices help engineers to analyse the characteristics of the ground being tested.

With this new system of probing directly into the earth, scientists should be able to measure quickly almost everything from the thickness of ice in the Arctic to the hardness of rock on the ocean floor.

# Earth Gun

# Gasoline Tree

latex-type substance, which could easily be refined into gasoline. Instead of waiting for Mother Nature to form oil deposits from decaying plants over millions of years, Dr. Calvin wondered whether scientists could plant a grove of these remarkable gasoline trees and tap them for their energy.

The plants seem to thrive in a hot dry climate such as that in the southwestern United States, and there is already a plan to plant the first experimental grove of avaloz trees near Riverside, California. Each acre of plants would produce between two and fifteen barrels of oil per year, at one-half the price of today's crude oil.

In the experimental stages, the plants will be tapped and milked, in the same way that rubber is taken from a rubber tree. Eventually, the plants may be trimmed like a gigantic hedge, and the petroleum-producing latex would be squeezed out of the trimmings with a powerful press.

Although it's too early to tell if this oil-growing technique will ever be commercially successful, it's possible that one day the stock market may be selling shares in oil orchards instead of oil wells.

**U**ntil recently, there seemed to be nothing we could do about the ever-increasing cost of oil and gasoline – that is, until a Nobel-Prize-winning chemist decided to take up gardening and grow his oil, instead of drilling for it.

Dr. Melvin Calvin of the University of California discovered that a Brazilian plant called the "avaloz" had the incredible ability to produce a

**A**gricultural scientists at the Zoological Institute in Cordoba, Spain, discovered that cows don't like bright light. In fact, on a hot day they get so irritated that they'd prefer to go hungry rather than graze in the sun.

Instead of getting the cows to change their habits, researchers have come up with an ingenious solution that keeps their cows munching on a sunny day: huge sun umbrellas mounted on wheels. Wherever the cows choose to graze, the mobile sun shield is pushed into position and the cows remain content, always in the shade.

Now that their milky complexions are safe from the sun, the Spanish cows are eating happily and putting on more weight than ever before.

Shade on Wheels

The beautiful city of Venice is threatened every year when high water levels flood in from the sea. Now, thanks to an ingenious experimental rubber dam developed by Arturo Colamussi of the University of Bologna, the historic city of Venice should have no trouble surviving the seasonal floods.

The dam, looking for all the world like a gigantic hot-water bottle, lies submerged and anchored on the sea bed when it's not in use. But when the weather gets rough and floods threaten the city, the dam fills with water and slowly rises to the surface to repel the heavy seas.

The system is controlled by a computer that forecasts high winds and tides and operates the dam automatically on the basis of this information. When the bad-weather alarm is triggered by the computer, high-speed-turbine pumping stations fill the submerged dam with water, establishing a bastion against the wind-whipped waves that normally cause the Venetian Lagoon to overflow its banks.

Not only is the new dam cheaper and quicker to install than any other system; but unlike a steel and concrete dam, which would spoil the scenic splendour of the Venetian waterways, the new rubber dam will stay out of sight when it's not needed, and it could help to preserve the beauty of Venice for another five hundred years.

**Venetian Dam**

## Body-Hair Testing

Every year millions of children are injured and crippled by doing nothing more than playing sports at school. The injury epidemic has reached such a high proportion in New York state that one out of every five children who play contact sports ends up in hospital.

After examining the situation, medical doctors and sports specialists decided that certain kids were getting hurt because their bodies weren't strong enough to take the punishment. Not all children mature on the same time schedule. Chronological age seems to be a poor indicator of a child's physical readiness to participate in a contact sport.

Since there's a specific point in time when a boy's body becomes a man's body, doctors in New York are now using a new way to examine boys who want to take up sports. They're no longer asking how old the child is, or worrying about height, weight, or the size of biceps.

The doctors examine hair, and it's not the hair on the head. Doctors are checking how much hair a boy has on his face, under his arms, and in the pubic area. Physical maturity, it seems, is a better indicator of readiness for a particular sport, no matter what the chronological age might be. This unique physical examination, combined with tests for strength, speed, agility, and endurance, now gives doctors and coaches a better chance to guide youngsters into the specific sports for which they're suited. It also means that sports-related injuries to young people are being reduced.

# Sick-Book Hospital

The old saying that a little knowledge is a dangerous thing can be taken literally, especially if the knowledge is found in certain kinds of books. It seems that old dusty books can become infected with microscopic creatures that can be spread to the reader, causing illness.

In order to remedy the problem, a library in Tallinn City in Estonia has established a "hospital" for infected books. When a "sick" book is diagnosed in the library, it's treated with a mixture of chemicals that kills the harmful bacteria. Only when the book is finally "cured" is it put back on the shelf.

But preventive medicine is still the byword of the book clinic. Librarians are beginning to treat large volumes of printed material well ahead of time, so that the books, manuscripts, and their readers will be fully protected against possible illness.

When a railway link was built recently in tropical northwestern Australia, the work slowed down when engineers encountered a strange and troublesome insect. It seems that the wooden railway ties supporting the track became a local delicacy for a band of voracious termites who lived along the route. The problem was doubly difficult because the railway ties looked perfectly normal; but in fact they were so rotten that they couldn't possibly support the weight of a train.

Researchers from the Australian Atomic Energy Commission developed a portable solution to cut down the termite hazard. It's a special car that rides slowly along the tracks and sends out a continuous beam of gamma rays toward the wooden railway ties. When the rays hit the ties and bounce back, they can be measured. Engineers can then instantly identify the ties that return faulty signals, indicating that the wood has been eaten away. Railway workers can then move in quickly to replace the faulty ties. The efficient gamma-ray track-checker has helped do away with the necessity of having men move on foot over thousands of miles of track to check for safety.

Gamma-Ray Track-Checker

Every spring in England, billions of flowering fruit trees have to be fertilized. Until recently, however, there seemed to be no way to guarantee that the job would be done. The main worker is the honey bee, who deposits small amounts of pollen on the blossoms that he visits while gathering nectar. But sometimes the bee isn't the most efficient employee. Although it takes only one teaspoonful of pollen to fertilize two million flowers, the bee would often leave on his nectar-gathering trips without any pollen at all.

A team of British scientists decided that it was about time to start producing labour-saving devices for insects, as well as for humans. They came up with a remarkable little invention: a special pollen dispenser for bees.

The dispenser, filled with pollen that the scientists have gathered and stored, is installed right at the opening of the hive. Every time the bee leaves, the dispenser is tripped, showering him with golden pollen. Whenever he touches a flower, the necessary pollination takes place.

But before the device could work, the bees had to be trained to use the dispenser. They had to learn how to get in and out through a special system of one-way doors, set up to make sure that the insects leave the hive with their shower of pollen and return through a different set of doors. The doors are controlled by a clever arrangement of springs. The bee can push himself out the "out" door; but he can't get back in through anything except the "in" door.

With the bees delighted to have half their work done for them, and with the new dispenser serving up as much pollen as the flowers could possibly use, scientists are looking forward to bumper crops of fruit in the future.

Museum of Natural Sciences, where they found that the bones of dinosaurs, mammoths, and ancient horses also contained significant traces of uranium. The scientists believe that because uranium is sometimes found diluted in ground water, these gigantic creatures must have sipped uranium-laden water and unwittingly left in their bones a prehistoric map to guide twentieth-century scientists toward new discoveries.

By examining museum records that show where the dinosaur bones came from, engineers have already made some small discoveries of uranium deposits in places where, otherwise, they never would have thought to look.

## Uranium Bone-Mining

Geologists and mining engineers are always trying to find new sources of ore as part of the continuing hunt for precious natural resources. Scientists from Canada's Department of Energy, Mines and Resources think that they've discovered a surprising new guide in the fossil section of the local museum. It seems that fossil bones of extinct animals can be of great help in the search for uranium.

When the bones of an extinct titanothere, a rhinoceros-like animal that lived in southern Saskatchewan some thirty million years ago, were uncovered in an ancient gravel bed, researchers discovered that the bones had a uranium content of nearly .2 per cent. Since uranium doesn't disappear from the bones after an animal dies, the geologists went to the

Outside Tucson, Arizona, you might catch a group of researchers dressed in white gowns, face masks, and surgical gloves, hard at work in an outdoor laboratory. They're not doctors, however, they're garbage students, sifting for science at the local dump. It's all part of an ongoing research project conducted by a team of anthropologists from the University of Arizona; the students are discovering how much food we consume and how much we throw away.

Every day like clockwork, the local garbage men set aside thirty-eight bags of garbage to be studied by the researchers. Each banana peel, broken bottle, and ripped newspaper is tagged and weighed, and the information is fed back into a computer data-bank.

Researchers now estimate that the people

# Garbage Students

of Tucson throw away more than ten thousand tons of edible food valued at twelve million dollars every single year. In fact, all the dogs in town could be fed just from the meat tossed out by the city's restaurants.

At a time when people in some parts of the world are malnourished, even starving to death, the university study could have far-reaching effects. By making people aware of Western society's tremendous waste, the project should encourage us to eat a little more and throw away a little less.

Speech problems in children often go undetected for many years, because there's no reliable way to check for such impairment when a child is very young. In England, a series of experiments with galloping horses has led to a new way of predicting whether or not a tiny baby is ever likely to have a speech problem.

The method was developed by a group of veterinary researchers who were studying the breathing patterns of horses, to try and pinpoint any defects that the animals might have when under stress. A special microphone was fitted directly around each horse's chest. The mike sent back to a tape recorder the sound of the horse's breathing, so that scientists could monitor the animal's breath rate. In one case, when the recording was slowed down researchers could hear a slight flutter, which indicated that the horse had a particular breathing defect.

Scientists who were attending to children with speech problems heard about the horse experiment and decided to apply the same idea to their own work. They built a similiar sound-detection device and used it to record the noises that babies make when nursing. Since a baby's sucking depends on well formed muscles and bones in the mouth, scientists can now determine whether the feeding sounds are completely normal. If there are any problems, doctors will now know well in advance and they'll be able to treat the babies even before they begin to speak.

# Horse Sensor

# Computerized

## Tailor

At Kyoto University in Japan, people who need to shop for clothes are starting to browse through the electronics laboratory of Dr. Toshiyuki Sakai. It seems that Dr. Sakai and his staff have been developing a computerized system that designs clothing. By simply entering the necessary wardrobe information through a computer terminal, it's now possible to select the size and shape of a chosen piece of clothing.

The customer stands in front of a television camera. Then, by using a series of data banks and programmed information, the computer displays on a television screen what the person will look like in his new clothes. If there's any problem, the clothing can be altered instantly or tailored to the customer's taste. As the computer makes all the necessary changes, the customer watches his television image changing right before his eyes — a blue shirt becomes green, a double-breasted jacket becomes single-breasted, or the shoulders get more padding.

Although still in the early stages of experimentation, the system has been so ingeniously produced that a fully computerized tailoring system will one day take the order, instantly show the customer what he looks like in the new outfit, make the necessary alterations, and then cut and sew the cloth to the required size and shape.

# Laser Teeth

Over 90 per cent of the people in the world are affected by tooth decay. No matter how often we brush, we still seem to get cavities. Those trips to the dentist may soon become fewer and farther between, however, thanks to a remarkable new technique that may turn cavities into a thing of the past.

Dr. Douglas Ruhlman, Professor of Dentistry at the University of California, has been firing laser beams into the mouths of his patients. With the new technique, Dr. Ruhlman first paints a tooth with a protective coating and applies a type of ceramic glaze. Then, using a flexible glass tube with a pinpoint focus, he aims a laser beam at the target tooth. When the beam hits the tooth, it heats the surface up to fifteen hundred degrees, and the glaze becomes permanently fused to the tooth enamel. The laser beam is on for only a fraction of a second, and the patient doesn't even feel the heat. The glaze covering seals the pores of the tooth enamel so completely that bacteria cannot get through the enamel. Decay can no longer eat away at the inside of the tooth and cause a cavity. So far, Dr. Ruhlman has been experimenting on older people who were about to lose their remaining teeth. The treatment has been so successful that he's already planning to test it on a group of three hundred children. Perhaps one day a single laser treatment may stop cavities for a lifetime, and that first trip to the dentist will become the last.

For most of us, on a clear night the stars look sharp and bright, in contrast to the black night-time sky. But for astronomers, even with their powerful telescopes the stars are not sharp enough, because the atmosphere surrounding the earth acts as a haze. In order to overcome this problem, research engineers and astronomers from the United States and Europe have developed an ingenious solution. Since we can't get rid of the atmosphere, the next best thing to do is to put a telescope on the other side of it.

With the use of precision gyroscopes, scientists are launching a large space telescope into orbit around the earth via the American space shuttle. Operated by ground command, the orbiting telescope will enable astronomers to see both planetary and extra-galactic worlds in a way never before thought possible. Research engineers from the United States National Aeronautics and Space Administration say that the orbiting space telescope is the most powerful in the world. It will provide pictures with thirty times more detail than those of any optical telescope found on earth, since the lens will no longer be handicapped by atmospheric haze.

# Orbiting Telescope

Every year, thousands of children are killed when they carelessly run onto the road. But British researchers have found that when children are hit by cars, it's not the actual impact that's fatal. Most fatal injuries result when the child is thrown under the wheels of the car or into the line of traffic. Automobile-design engineers felt that if a child who was hit could be prevented from falling into a more dangerous position, the injuries wouldn't be as severe. The answer to the problem is a clever safety device that catches children when they're hit. Across the front bumper of the car engineers have fashioned a highly sensitive, spring-loaded bar. The moment the bar makes contact with something, it shoots forward and upward. Now, if a child runs onto the street and gets hit by a car, the pedestrian catcher shoots out, catches the small body, and throws it up to the safety of the car's hood.

If tests continue to be successful, the engineers hope to introduce the pedestrian catcher on all British cars in the very near future.

# Pedestrian Catcher

# Scoop Boat

Water sports such as speed-boat racing and water skiing are great fun, until you end up in the drink. An injured racing driver, for example, faces the danger of further injury from other speed boats.

With conventional rescue craft, the victim has to be pulled over the side – a practice that may aggravate any injuries he has already sustained. But British engineers have come up with an ingenious rescue boat that actually scoops the marooned driver out of the water, like a fish in a net. The front end of the boat swings down like a landing craft and floats the survivor safely into the boat on a gentle cushion of water.

The secret of the boat's construction lies in a double hull filled with buoyant foam that makes the boat unsinkable, no matter how much water comes in with the victim. As soon as the injured person is safely on board, the boat moves off, and the water that was taken on during the rescue is pumped out through special outlets. At the dock, the front-end ramp is gently lowered again, so a stretcher can be manoeuvred into the boat and under the injured person.

Preliminary tests have been so successful that it may not be long before the scoop boat becomes standard equipment for water safety patrols everywhere.

# Jet Streams of Printing Ink

Although an electric typewriter may be a model of efficiency for a secretary, to scientists at the IBM Yorktown Heights Research Centre it's a slow and inefficient way of printing information. They are experimenting with a new form of printing that does away with ribbons and bulky metal parts. The creation is an ink-jet printer, with no hammers and no ribbons. Because it has no moving parts it won't wear out or vibrate, and it is practically silent.

The new ink-delivery system moves only the ink itself, in the form of tiny droplets, from nozzles to the paper. Under computer control, minute globules of ink some two-thousandths of an inch thick speed through an electromagnetic field onto paper, at the rate of a hundred thousand drops a second from each nozzle. The drops travel at a speed of forty feet per second.

Today, computer print-out machines can automatically type about thirty numbers per second. With the new ink-jet system, two thousand numbers can be produced every second, and the quality is perfect every time. Printing with jet streams of ink could one day turn the electric typewriter into a curious twentieth-century antique.

# Cow Credit Card

A day in the life of a milk cow has always been a very simple existence. The only complication occurs at feeding time. Some cows eat too quickly, while others dawdle around, nibbling at the grain. But in order to produce the most milk, each cow must satisfy its own individual dietary requirements. Recently, animal researchers have come up with a system that makes it possible to ensure that all cattle eat properly.

Each cow is given a personal credit card. The card is really an electronic device that's hooked onto the cow's collar. When the animal wants something to eat, she wanders over to specially designed stalls in the barnyard and pokes her head through a hole in the feed trough. The credit card around her neck sends out a coded radio signal, which activates a feed dispenser. It sends down the grain as quickly as the cow wants to eat, because each card is individually programmed.

But if a cow doesn't want to eat everything at one sitting, nothing is wasted. She just walks away and comes back again when she's hungry. The credit-card system is based on a twelve-hour schedule; food is doled out whenever the cow wants to eat, until the twelve-hour ration has been used up. After that, no matter how often the cow pokes her head into the trough, no more food will come through until the next time period. With the new device, milk production is way up, and the cows seem to have taken to the credit-card system almost as well as people have.

# Cow Radio

In the cattle country of western New Mexico, there's a special steer who stands out from the rest of the herd. He can tell you his temperature at the push of a button, and he can't be stolen by cattle rustlers. Veterinary researchers at the Los Alamos Scientific Laboratory have developed an electronic system that can tell ranchers instantly whether their cattle are healthy or sick. By planting a tiny electronic radio in the shoulder of a steer, the scientists can tune into the wired animal. When they aim a small antenna at the steer, the transmitter sends back a signal that gives his temperature in a tenth of a second. If an infectious disease should hit a herd of "wired" steers, ranchers can weed out the sick ones long before the rest of the herd become infected.

In another development of the same technique, researchers have discovered a new way of identifying cattle without the painful method of branding with a hot iron. Before they implant the radio transmitter, they wire it to transmit a special electronic message. Now, if a rancher sees a cow wandering down the road, he only has to turn on his radio to find out who is the rightful owner.

**T**here's a new breed of medical assistant taking some of the drudgery out of working in hospital wards. He's a rolling robot called "Amscar". He moves silently and automatically throughout the hospital, and goes wherever he's told to go.

Developed by research engineers at the American Sterilizer Company in Ontario, this device can carry everything from soiled dishes to sterilized operating linen to any part of the hospital. And Amscar is very easy to operate. You just set the dial to his destination, press the start button, and the robot does all the rest.

Amscar is automatically guided by an invisible electronic track that is cut into the floor at the time the hospital is built. The robot has been so cleverly produced that he can call his own elevator and even instruct the elevator to take him to the right floor. If several robots leave the elevator together, they line up in an orderly fashion until space becomes available.

To be certain that the new system is completely safe, engineers designed a soft rubber-bumper system that instantly stops the robot if he should

happen to touch anyone; and if any mechanical part breaks, Amscar can be taken off his track and sent back to the shop for instant repairs.

The system is constantly monitored on a display panel, where tiny lights indicate the specific location of every working robot. After each trip through the hospital, the robots line up to be washed in a processing unit that's very similar to a carwash. When the Amscars come out, doctors know they've been completely sanitized and are ready once again to do their daily rounds through the hospital wards.

South Pole Personality

I f you think you're dull, introverted, and very messy, you'd be a perfect candidate for work at the South Pole. This personality profile is a result of twenty years of observation by psychologists and physiologists who are faced with the problem of sending the most suitable people to work at tracking stations or scientific outposts in the Antarctic.

In the early days of polar exploration, almost anybody who was healthy and crazy enough could go. But it takes more than a pioneering spirit to live through the long polar night. In order to make a healthy adjustment to life in the isolated regions of the polar caps, the individual should be self-sufficient, introverted, have few outside interests, and be comfortable about being somewhat messy. This personality profile presently serves as a guide for screening potential workers at the South Pole.

# Electromagnetic Operation

Recently, a two-year-old Russian boy had a screw lodged in his lungs, and doctors were faced with the dangerous possibility of major lung surgery. One of the doctors, Yakov Vertlib, came up with a brilliant idea. Instead of subjecting the baby to the trauma of major surgery, he decided to make use of magnetism.

The team of doctors had to work fast. They placed an urgent order for a tiny electromagnet that would be lowered into the boy's body through a medical device called a "bronchoscope". When the magnet was in place inside the lungs, the current was turned on and it attracted the screw. By careful, delicate manipulations, the screw was slowly pulled up past the throat and out through the mouth.

Russian doctors now believe that this new magnetic-surgery technique may solve similar medical problems in the future, without the use of a scalpel.

# Mouse-Control Pill

When mice threaten to walk off with the cheese, you can feed them poison, set up a mousetrap, or call in the Pied Piper. Or you can write to the Ecology Research Center at Miami University for a mouse-control pill.

For years, poison was used successfully to control the mouse population in homes, until it was discovered that certain chemicals were actually breeding a race of Super Mice. These mice became so strong that they could grow and even breed while eating nothing but a well known commercial poison. To combat these Mighty Mice, research mouseologists have discovered a chemical that seems to work like a birth-control pill. Called diethylstilbesterol, or DES, it's a female sex hormone that seems to make male mammals sterile. The chemical was put in a peanut butter sandwich and fed to mice experimentally and, after only ten weeks, it worked so well that the mouse population was cut down almost to zero.

If early tests are any indication, householders may soon turn their mousetraps into paperweights, since the pitter-patter of little mouse feet may no longer be heard in the pantry.

41

# Hawaiian Energy

Geological scientists are now attempting to harness the power of the earth. At the University of Hawaii, researchers are digging a shaft more than a mile into the ground in order to tap an underground body of water that's been heated past the boiling point by molten rock, which feeds Hawaii's five volcanoes.

Because the pressure under the earth's surface is so intense, the superheated water stays in a liquid state. But once it gets above ground, the water instantly flashes into a searing blast of steam – steam that's going to make electricity. By automatically channeling the continual blast of steam through a huge turbine, electricity will be created and fed into the conventional power grid. Scientists believe that this new system will produce a very inexpensive source of energy. If so, Hawaii's electricity bills may be on the way down.

# Pneumatic Fire-Fighter

**E**ach year fire costs us millions of dollars in destroyed property. The cost in human lives is even greater. In an effort to save the lives of fire-fighters, British scientists think they may have come up with a way to use fire-fighting expertise while keeping it a safe distance from the fire. They've invented a fire-fighting robot.

The real fire-fighter sits at a safe distance from the blaze and operates the robot by remote control. If the machine is fighting at close range, the operator chooses a very fine spray. If the robot is working at long distances away from the blaze, the operator will select a jet of water that is more powerful than a human could ever handle. Foam, too, can be shot out at a rate of seven hundred gallons a minute, a thrust large enough to bring even the most dangerous oil and gas blazes quickly under control.

As a safety measure, the fire-fighting robot runs on compressed air instead of electricity, so that sparks cannot set off an explosion. In the future, all fire-fighters may be able to sit in perfect safety, while expendable machines take on all the risks of putting out the fire.

**W**hen all the trees in a forest have been cut down, new seedlings must be planted by hand so that the forest will grow again. But it takes a long time to replant a forest, and recently it's been getting harder than ever to find enough people to do the job.

Scientists at the University of British Columbia's Research Forest have developed a new way of planting trees that almost totally eliminates human hands. The seedlings are placed in plastic containers shaped like bombs. Thousands of these seed-bombs are loaded onto a plane to be dropped over the target site. When they reach their destination, the seed-bombs are released into the air at intervals, landing in the ground upright and ready to grow.

Forestry researcher Dr. John Walters says that in a thousand-acre forest, it usually takes ten men one hundred days to plant the seedlings. But with the new seed-bombs, it takes only one man a single day to do the same job.

Forest Seed-Bombs

Animal researchers in New Zealand have proven beyond a doubt that sheep are social snobs. During the mating season, a team of animal psychologists were baffled when an ordinary ram was rejected by a whole flock of ewes. At first, the researchers thought that the ram was sterile. But after further study, they discovered a completely different reason.

It seems that sheep are social climbers. In a scientific experiment, the ram in question tried to pick the strongest ewe for a mate, but she rejected him; apparently, he just didn't have enough class. On the next mating attempt, however, the ram was sent in with a bunch of his friends. This time, all the sheep mated successfully and there were no rejections.

It seems that the dominant female will mate only with the dominant male and, once that has happened, the other partners feel more comfortable about finding their proper place in the social order.

# Sheep Social Order

# Golden Windows

If you want to reduce your heating bills, it might be a good idea to install new windows – that is, windows of gold.

This idea was recently proposed at a meeting of the American Chemical Society during a discussion on solar energy. It seems that we lose a lot of heat through glass panes and storm windows. But chemical researchers have discovered that a thin film of gold laid directly on the window allows all the light to go through, while keeping all the heat inside where it's needed.

Dr. John Fan of the Massachusetts Institute of Technology says that a golden layer on the glass could reduce heating losses by 50 per cent. Surprising as it may seem, the required gold film would be so thin that cost does not seem to be a major factor.

## Glaucoma Eye-Pill

Until recently, doctors usually treated glaucoma patients with a type of medication that sometimes produced serious side effects, such as blurred vision.

Now, research chemists at the Alza Pharmaceutical Company in Palo Alto, California, have developed a revolutionary new system of delivering the drug directly to the eye, without danger of any side effects. The system is really a tiny pill that fits comfortably underneath the lower lid of the eye. It holds a reservoir of medicine and releases tiny amounts of the drug directly to the eye in a continuous and precisely measured dosage, day and night for one week.

*After six years of continuous research and experimental testing, the new glaucoma eye-pill is available commercially, providing a treatment more efficient than ever before.*

At Japan's National Research and Development Centre, computers have been developed that can watch for and recognize two-dimensional objects such as printed letters or geometric shapes. The computer uses a television-camera eye to analyse the image, and then searches its memory banks until recognition is definite. The new system also hears and recognizes human speech patterns.

As a result of this specialized research, revolutionary new ways to help the handicapped are being developed.

Electronic eyes for the blind use a computerized camera that changes what it "sees" into a shape that the blind person can feel. And with the help of a computer and tiny sensors matched to the muscles of the arm, scientists have constructed a bionic hand that works just like a living hand. It's connected to nerve endings in the disabled person's arm and actually responds to commands from the brain.

It may not be long before a computer system can really think for itself, and maybe one day each computer will begin to develop its own distinctive personality.

# Aquaculture

If you take a pond, add some fish, stir in a pinch of plankton, and mix with liberal amounts of raw manure, you've got the latest culinary offering served up by the world of science. It's called "aquaculture", and this basic recipe may be one of the best ways to provide food for people.

Dr. Homer Buck, an aquatic biologist, is experimenting with a never-ending natural cycle that turns barnyard waste into good, wholesome food. At the Sam A. Parr Fisheries Research Centre near Kinmundy, Illinois, researchers are dumping pig manure into a series of ponds and pools. Tiny plankton algae grow in the rich manure, while keeping the water clean and safe. Small Chinese silver carp feed on the algae by swimming around the tanks with their mouths open. In no time at all, the small fingerling fish turn into edible beauties weighing close to eight pounds each.

Dr. Buck says that the fish are delicious. And the firm, light flesh is as good as anything you can buy in your local fish market.

# Plant Anti-perspirant

In a world where water can be a very scarce commodity, it come surprise to learn that some of the worst water-wasters around are ordinary green plants. Of all the water that plants draw up from their roots, only about half is necessary for growth; the other half is given off in plant "perspiration".

Plants, like humans, have pores through which they can lose water, and some highly developed plants shed water at an almost unbelievable rate. British plant researchers at Lancaster University who were looking for a way to control these perspiring plants came up with a very logical solution to the problem. They took a tip from a television roll-on deodorant commercial and devised an efficient plant anti-perspirant. Called "Formula F", the special solution is painted on the leaves, causing the pores to close. Only one application is needed to keep the plants dry for several days, and since Formula F is designed to act only on the cells that regulate the pores, the rest of the plant is unaffected.

Tests proved that plants treated with Formula F needed only half as much water as they did before treatment. During drought conditions, that could be a very important statistic. It seems that farmers may have fewer worries about irrigation as soon as researchers devise an efficient way to paint the plant anti-perspirant on all the leaves in acres and acres of crops.

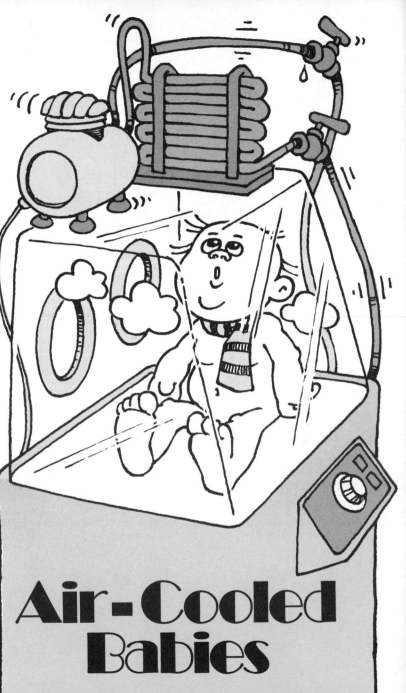

**S**ometimes newborn infants have serious problems with their tiny hearts and require open-heart surgery. During the operation, the normal functions of the continually beating organ must be taken over by the remarkable heart-lung machine. But it's not an easy job to switch from the heart to a machine. Doctors must first cool down the baby's blood temperature, so that the brain won't require as much oxygen as it normally does.

In the past, doctors had to rely on icepacks to bring the baby's body temperature down to the required level, but this method had a lot of serious disadvantages. Icepacks produced uneven cooling around the body, and often it took too long for the whole body to be cooled. Furthermore, after the operation, the babies not only had to recover from the surgery; sometimes they also had frostbite, thanks to the icepacks.

Faced with these problems, Dr. Sambamurthy Subramanian, a cardiovascular surgeon at Children's Hospital in Buffalo, New York, decided he had a better idea. He took an ordinary incubator from the maternity ward and made some major changes. The result is the world's first air-cooled chamber that can lower a baby's temperature evenly. Designed on the same principle as the household refrigerator, but with the addition of an air-flow unit, the remarkable chamber cools down the baby while keeping a constant check on the child's internal temperature.

Doctors at the Hospital for Sick Children in Toronto have already used the air-cooled chamber in forty open-heart-surgery operations, and at last report, the babies are all doing fine.

# Air-Cooled Babies

# Earology

If someone should come up to you and ask for a picture of your ear, don't laugh or rush away. He just might be Alfred V. Iannarelli of the University of California, the world's most ardent classifier of ears, and developer of a new science called "earology". He claims that no two human ears are exactly alike. Through his study of ear pictures, he discovered that there are certain key identification points on the external ear that remain the same throughout our lives.

By comparing the ear-identity pictures with the ears of someone who, for some reason, can't be identified by file photographs, a definite identification could be made. The system isn't intended to replace fingerprints, but only to supplement them in cases where fingerprints might be damaged or destroyed.

The most famous example of identification by earology to date is the verification of a picture of Mao Tse-tung swimming in the sea, at a time when there was a rumour that the Chinese leader was dead. Mr. Iannarelli says that interest in his work seems to be building, since both the CIA and FBI have used his system successfully. Others, such as the Canadian RCMP, are now considering it.

In the continual hunt for precious mineral resources, scientists have discovered a new kind of Geiger counter. It's not made of electronic parts and moving dials; it has four legs, a soft wet nose, and a tail that wags when it makes a strike.

Research engineers with the Finnish Geological Survey believe that a dog's uncanny sense of smell can be trained to detect mineral deposits, even if they're well hidden in the earth. In an isolated region just west of Kuipio, a specially trained basset hound called Vahti wagged his tail with glee and managed to sniff out a sulphur deposit in almost no time at all. It would have taken a miner many days of hard searching and digging before he found the same deposit.

Dogs in other parts of Scandinavia are finding mineral deposits as well. In Sweden, a dog named Dolli sniffed out huge boulders that contained small traces of copper. On further examination, the Swedish geologists realized to their surprise that Dolli had indeed managed to track down a large vein of copper ore that had been hidden from miners for centuries.

Although geologists are not yet turning in their research tools and instruments, they feel they've found a valuable new friend in their hunt for mineral resources, and a new companion to keep them company over those long days on the road to discovery.

# Doggy Gold Rush

# Nutty Mutts

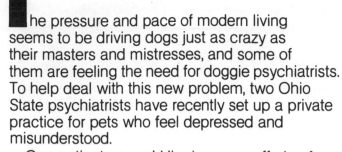

The pressure and pace of modern living seems to be driving dogs just as crazy as their masters and mistresses, and some of them are feeling the need for doggie psychiatrists. To help deal with this new problem, two Ohio State psychiatrists have recently set up a private practice for pets who feel depressed and misunderstood.

One patient named Higgins was suffering from an overwhelming fear of storms. All the psychiatrists had to do was give him a special treat – a small dish of ice cream – while they played tape recordings of thunderstorms at slowly increasing volume. In a very short time, Higgins learned to associate the sound of a storm with getting a treat. At last report, every time there was a storm Higgins was seen wagging his tail.

And for pets who become destructive, the psychiatrists have a positive solution. They suggest that you lie in ambush behind your dog's favourite target. When he starts to chew or scratch on that special piece of furniture, you zap him with a sudden blast from a water pistol. It doesn't really hurt, and your pet soon learns to leave that valuable furniture alone.

Traffic congestion in Japan's heavily populated cities continues to get worse as the years go by. In Tokyo alone, 268 main intersections face horrendous traffic jams, pollution, and smog every day. Thanks to a team of Japanese engineers who have developed a computerized traffic-control system, drivers now know where to go to avoid the worst congestion.

A test car in the new system is fitted with a miniature computer hooked up by radio to the central station, which continually monitors traffic conditions throughout the city. The driver inserts the code of his destination into the control system of his car, like a pilot filing his flight plan. A display panel on the dashboard gives him instructions as he approaches each intersection: turn right, turn left, go straight ahead, or go back. Simply by following these instructions as he goes along, the driver will reach his destination in the shortest possible time.

Nearby accidents or emergencies are reported to the driver through his car radio, even if it's not turned on. And if he fails to obey road signs or starts to drive carelessly, the little computer brings him up short with a stern reprimand.

Although the work has so far been largely experimental, there are already three hundred computerized cars ready to be tested. Designers are hoping to implement the automated system in one urban district of Tokyo in the very near future, so that one day all drivers may benefit from computerized traffic control.

Computerized Car-Control

# Cheeping Chicks

Soviet chicken breeders have been scratching their heads for years, trying to find a faster way to separate future hens and roosters in the fluffy yellow mass of newly hatched baby chicks. Because only female chickens lay eggs, the breeders aren't particularly interested in wasting feed on unproductive male chicks. But which is which? Determination of sex has to be done by hand and it's a very time-consuming process.

Russian researchers at the Bioenergetic Laboratory of the Volgograd Agricultural Institute have finally hit upon a way to tell a chick, just by its cheep. Although the human ear can't pick up the difference, it seems that the male chick's cheep is not the same as the female's. By using a special electronic hearing device, the scientists can now sort the chicks according to whether they're soprano or bass. The females then go down one passageway and the males down another.

As long as the male chicks don't get wise and start studying voice impressions, Soviet breeders should have a much easier time separating the boys from the girls.

For many years, biomedical engineers have been searching for some way to help deaf people hear, especially people who are so deaf that they can't be helped by a hearing aid. Although researchers have had limited success with implanting a single electrode in the ear, this traditional approach allows patients to hear sound on a single frequency only. The implant helps the deaf to hear things like doorbells and telephones. But it is much too elementary for sophisticated sounds like human speech.

With the help of two deaf volunteers, scientists at the Institute of Biomedical Engineering at the University of Utah think that they may be on the way to developing a complete artificial hearing system. The new system involves placing a series of six electrodes along the coiled membrane of the inner ear.

A volunteer with only one deaf ear has been wearing the electrode implants for over a year and hears sounds of varying pitch and loudness. To help researchers understand exactly what he's hearing, he finds a note on a piano keyboard, matching with his good ear what he hears in the deaf ear.

With the success of these experiments, the researchers have a clearer understanding of how electrical stimulation patterns cause variations in pitch and loudness. They hope to develop a computerized and miniaturized portable hearing device that will one day provide the deaf with the gift of sound.

News of a significant breakthrough in helping the blind to see has come from researchers at the University of Utah and the University of Western Ontario. A team of neuroscientists has developed an extraordinary computerized system that virtually restores sight by by-passing the injured eyes. Special electrodes are implanted in a blind patient's visual cortex, the area of the brain at the back of the head where signals from the eyes are usually received. The electrodes are connected directly to a computer.

In one experiment, the patient was hooked up to a television camera, which picked up simple images and sent them directly to the visual cortex by means of computer signals. In another, the electrodes were attached to braille letters of the alphabet. In each case, the brain responded as if it were receiving a message from the patient's eyes, and the patient could tell what he was seeing.

The research team is now working on an intricate system that blind people could use continually. This system would consist of a tiny camera fitted into the eyesocket. The camera would send visual signals to a miniature computer worn in a pair of eyeglasses. In turn, the computer would send the signals to the electrodes at the back of the brain and the patient would actually be able to "see".

**Artificial Vision**

Artificial Vision

Artificial Vision

Artificial Vision

If your dog ever tangles with a skunk, don't try to give him a bath – give him a home permanent. This bizarre treatment was recently tried by Dr. George Loeb, of University College in North Wales, when his dog came home smelling of skunk. The awful smell brought on desperate measures, and Dr. Loeb gave his unhappy dog a quick home permanent. Much to his surprise, the chemical lotion worked so well that the skunk smell completely disappeared.

The offensive ingredient in the skunk smell is based on sulphur, also an ingredient in stink bombs and rotten eggs. And the chemical in permanent solutions that breaks down hair fibre enough to curl it also breaks down the sulphur compound, and the smell ceases to exist.

So, remember the home permanent if your pet ever exchanges hostilities with a skunk. But if the dog has hair too short for curling, the old tried and true remedy, tomato juice, is still a reliable way to get rid of the terrible smell – not only for dogs, but for children, as well.

Doggie Deodorant

# Bread Diet

If you're overweight and want to shed some excess pounds, start eating bread, and lots of it, according to Dr. Olaf Mickelsen, Professor of Food Science and Human Nutrition at Michigan State University. The experimental bread diet worked for university volunteers, who lost an average of 16.5 pounds over an eight-week period.

Dr. Mickelsen says that the diet is really simplicity itself. Each volunteer ate twelve slices of bread daily, as well as whatever else he or she wanted, even snacks and ice cream. It seems that all that bread makes you feel so full that it's difficult to eat very much else, and the total number of calories consumed is kept down to a comfortable minimum.

The study also showed that the starch in the bread prevented the side effects of nausea and headache, which sometimes occur during a diet. The bread diet also lowered the serum cholesterol level in the volunteers, an important consideration for overweight people who have heart problems and are thinking of losing weight. But before you rush out to buy those loaves of bread, Dr. Mickelsen makes it very clear that you must check with your doctor to make sure that the diet's right for you.

# Pollution Flower-Power

The water hyacinth has long been admired for its natural beauty. But today it's not just another pretty flower. It's hard at work fighting pollution.

It seems that the water hyacinth loves sewage. Give the hyacinth a stretch of water that's polluted with sewage, and the hungry flower starts sopping up the pollution with gusto. This beautiful garbage-cleaner works so well that it can absorb such toxic chemicals as lead, mercury, and strontium 90.

And that's exactly what it's doing in an experimental water-hyacinth waste project in Bay St. Louis, Mississippi, where research chemists are studying the flower-power of the mighty cleaners. In a forty-acre lagoon filled with sewage from six thousand households, there are seven acres of hard-working plants cleaning up the murky, smelly water. Believe it or not, they're so effective that the sewage is now fit to drink. The hyacinth also grows so quickly in polluted water that researchers are able to gather sixteen tons of hyacinth per acre every single day. But what do you do with sixteen tons of water hyacinth? Well, you just put them right back to work. Once the plants are cleaned and dried, they are so rich in mineral content from the sewage that they can be used as a highly effective fertilizer, and they can even serve as a source of food for livestock.

It's going to be harder than ever to forge a signature and get away with it.

Research scientists at the National Physical Laboratory in Britain have developed the first foolproof system for catching a forger, almost before the ink is dry. The suspected signature is scanned by computer and compared with a sample genuine signature. The result is an automatic determination of whether the signature is authentic or fraudulent, with as much certainty as the determination of a fingerprint.

The system is already in use as a security check in England. It involves two basic steps. The specimen signature is written on an electronic pad, which sends the characteristics of the writing to a computer. When someone signs his name, an electronic comparison of the new signature with the stored signature immediately reveals any discrepancies, not only in the shape of the letters, but also in the rhythm of the writing. So many different aspects of handwriting can now be analysed that the system makes it almost impossible to sign someone else's name and get away with it.

Forged Signatures

# Midnight Munching

When barnyard animals go to bed, they usually like a midnight snack. But sometimes they get so hungry that they start munching on the straw that's supposed to be their bedding. In these days of rising farming costs, the bedtime munching is becoming an expensive problem.

Researchers at the Canadian Department of Agriculture recently found a solution in the daily newspaper. After assuring themselves that there were no dangerous chemicals in the paper, the researchers tried old, shredded newspapers as bedding in the stalls. When morning came, the cows looked contented, and it's no wonder. After polishing off 10 per cent of the tasty stuff, they managed to get a good night's sleep.

Agricultural researchers are confident that the use of old newspaper as barnyard bedding will save the Canadian farmer thousands of dollars every year.

Every night, on highways all over the world, little nocturnal animals are being killed by cars and trucks. Researchers at the Austrian Academy of Sciences realized that there must be a solution to this nightly carnage. They solved the problem when they discovered how to make use of a very basic fear.

All small creatures are afraid of threatening eyes, and of the colour red. Special studies showed that red warning reflectors installed on many Austrian roadways could keep the animals off the road when a car was coming. The reflection of the approaching headlights in the reflectors looks like red, gleaming eyes along the roadside. Any small animal coming up out of the woods becomes frightened at the sight and turns back to safety. Once the car passes by, the red eyes disappear, and the animal can cross the road without harm.

Officials at the academy say that after a test run of only six months, animal mortality has been dramatically reduced by as much as 80 per cent, which is good news not only for the animals but also for the tender-hearted drivers.

# Animal Reflectors

**F**or years, British farmers have had trouble harvesting potatoes with machinery that was too rough for the job. The mechanical harvester was

# Tennis Ball Potato

mashing nearly 30 per cent of the potatoes before they ever got to market. Recently, a research scientist had a crafty idea. He took a tennis ball and painted it white. Inside it he inserted a tiny radio transmitter with a spring-loaded alarm. When he threw his special tennis ball into a potato patch, the harvesting machine collected it along with all the real potatoes, but this one complained when it received rough treatment! Whenever the tennis ball was hit too hard, the tiny transmitter sent a signal back to the central office. These insistent complaints soon showed where the trouble spots were, and by redesigning each danger point to soften the blows, engineers have reduced potato losses by 50 per cent, thanks to this electronic spy in a tennis ball.

**T**here was once a little girl named Goldilocks who knew something that researchers at Purdue University in Lafayette, Indiana, have only just discovered: that a soft, comfortable chair isn't always "just right".

Doctors Charlan Graff and Marjorie Inman of the university's School of Home Economics discovered in a recent study that people unconsciously choose their chairs according to how they feel and what they have to do at the moment.

If a person is going to eat lunch with a large group or take part in a debate, he or she automatically selects a hard, straight-backed, uncomfortable chair. The simpler and the harder the chair, the more it makes us feel that we stand out in the group. People who want to have a quiet, intimate talk about feelings with a friend move to a soft, comfortable chair. The plush chair provides some physical relief from the intense feelings and emotions in a highly personal conversation. Rocking chairs are good, too, since they soothe us and give us a chance to move in space, which makes some people feel less lonely when they're by themselves.

Dr. Graff concludes that by knowing how to choose funiture for its comfort index, we can make our homes more restful and soothing places for ourselves and our friends.

Friendly
Furniture

# Aquapolis

If crowded apartment living is getting you down, why not plan to take an ocean cruise on Aquapolis, the floating city of the future? Designed by the Japanese government for the first International Ocean Exposition, Aquapolis is a completely self-sufficient environment on the sea.

Weighing over thirteen thousand tons, this floating city is the largest structure of its kind in the world. Its beautiful living quarters can be completely enclosed, and the whole city can be submerged to a depth of thirty-two metres below the surface, to protect the inhabitants from rain, storms, and hurricanes. Aquapolis has its own power and waste-disposal systems, and even an experimental fish farm.

The Japanese know the real meaning of overcrowding and pollution, and their scientists see Aquapolis as more than a dream city. To them, it may provide an effective way to solve population problems of the future by building whole cities at sea.

In France, television has sunk to new depths – about four thousand feet below sea level. A team of French scientists from the Ionized Gas Laboratory at the National Institute of Nuclear Science and Technology has developed an experimental system that can automatically send television pictures from any point beneath the sea. It's made possible by a new device called an "ionophone", a special transmitter that sends television pictures by means of ultrasonic sound waves.

Until recently, underwater researchers had many problems sending television pictures, because the camera had to be connected to a ship on the surface by means of a long and heavy cable. But the ionophone can send remote pictures back to the surface without the use of any heavy connecting wires. Although the ultrasonic waves have to travel slowly through hundreds of feet of water, the sound waves remain intact. When they reach the receiver, they are easily changed into a television picture.

French scientists are hopeful that the new device will not only allow television transmissions from any underwater depth, but also allow pictures to be sent from one subsea craft directly to another.

Deep-Sea TV

69

# Cuddling Preemies

When a premature baby is born, doctors usually place the tiny, helpless child in an incubator to protect it from infection and disease. Even after the baby is released from the incubator, parents and nurses tend to treat the frail infant with more caution than they would a normal baby. But the lack of physical contact, it seems, may be detrimental to the baby's growth and development. Dr. Ruth Rue, who has been working with premature babies in a Dallas hospital, decided to see what would happen if hospital staff changed their behaviour toward premature babies. A group of specially trained nurses taught the mothers how to give their babies stroking, rocking, and massaging treatments, and the mothers carried out the instructions four times a day for fifteen minutes a day, over a period of a month.

When the premature babies were four months old, tests showed that infants who had received the touching and cuddling treatment displayed greater development than babies who hadn't. The test group gained more weight and scored higher in mental functioning. Dr. Rice recommends that mothers be allowed to massage, cuddle, and talk to their babies, even if the infants are still in the incubator. To prevent infection, the mothers could wear caps and gowns in the same way nurses do. Even though science has come a long way in the care and protection of infants, there still seems to be no substitute for a mother's love.

A baby born prematurely sometimes has difficulty breathing by himself. To help him, attending doctors may have to put a respirator mask over the tiny face. But this life-saving equipment brings its own problems, because the baby has a very fragile skull. The straps that hold the facemask on may actually cut into the tiny head.

Doctors at the Neonatal Unit of London's University College Hospital struggled with this problem until one of them came up with a new idea. Taking a piece of elastic tubular netting that is used to hold an intravenous-drip needle in place on an adult arm or leg, he cut the netting into the shape of a small hairnet. By fitting the netting right over the baby's head, facemask and all, he had a firm anchor for the equipment, and the pressure was safely and evenly distributed over the entire head.

The plastic hairnet for premature babies is proving extremely successful, and very easy to use. In fact, the other doctors are wondering why no one had ever thought of it before.

# Hairnet Holder for Preemies

# Radar Moths

**B**ats, it seems, have always been fond of certain juicy, night-flying moths, which they find in an instant by using highly developed radar-like instincts. To combat this, moths have been using their ultrasonic ears. When they hear the sound of a bat's hunting signal, they immediately set up evasive tactics. They abandon normal flight patterns and perform violent loops and twists. Sometimes they even plummet straight to the ground and play dead. The bat has to become an acrobat as it lunges and flips, trying to trap the moth in its wings like a baseball catcher.

Other moths have developed ultrasonic jamming devices. When the bats attack, the moths emit high, clicking sounds that send the attackers into a tailspin. The bats are thrown completely off target, while the moths make their getaway.

Nature seems to have struck a balance so that enough moths escape and the species survives; enough moths are eaten so that the bats don't go hungry.

Humans have now entered this ultrasonic war and are using the moths' own weapons against them as a means of effective insect control. Researchers at the Canadian Department of Agriculture, for example, have been looking for ways to help the farmer get rid of destructive moths that ruin millions of dollars worth of crops. In one experiment, they set up ultrasonic transmitters at both ends of a cornfield. The beams disrupted the moths' normal way of life so much that they couldn't eat and, at the end of the summer, crop damage by moths was reduced by 20 per cent.

If you've got children and you're looking for a new apartment, make sure you get a place on the top floor. Dr. John M. Mills, a teacher of speech pathology at Syracuse University, recently conducted a study that showed that children living on upper floors of apartment buildings have a lot less trouble understanding speech and learning to read than do their friends on lower floors.

Dr. Mills believes that the explanation lies in noise. Lower floors have a much higher noise level. Over a long period of time, this noise interferes with the way a child learns to listen.

While an adult can quite easily adjust to noise levels, young children learning to read or to understand speech can be so distracted that their learning is seriously hampered.

Another side effect of noise levels is that families on lower floors have fewer conversations, and the less the children were talked to, the less they understood.

So, for happier families and better learning, move to the top. Of course, if everyone follows this advice, we may have created another problem: what to do with all the empty bottom floors.

Upper Floor Smarties

What could help save the endangered sperm whale, make cars run better, and provide much-needed work for the American Indian? It's a ten-foot desert plant with leathery leaves and it's called the "jojoba".

Scientists first looked at the strange plant in 1920, when researchers at the Boyce Thompson Arboretum in Superior, Arizona, were caught without oil on a very hot day. It seems their office fan was squeaking so badly that in desperation, one of the researchers went outside and collected a colorless waxy oil from a jojoba plant growing nearby. The squeak was fixed, and history was in the making.

The jojoba produces an oil that has the same chemical properties as the oil taken from sperm whales. Until recently, sperm-whale oil was used as the main lubricant in the automatic transmission of a car. Every year we used fifty-five million pounds of it in our cars. After the sperm whale was declared an endangered species, no suitable synthetic substitute was found that works as well.

That is, until they found the jojoba. Its oil is very stable. It resists impurities and it's very, very slippery. If early testing is any indication, thousands of acres of arid land in southwestern United States will soon be growing the hardy jojoba plant, and car engineers will have the perfect substitute for sperm-whale oil.

# Shoeless Salvation

If you suffer from corns, hammer toes, bunions, ingrown toenails, or athletes foot, here's the latest news from the world of medicine: go barefoot. Dr. Paul W. Brand, an orthopedic surgeon who's worked for thirty years in India and Ethiopia, has seen a lot of bare feet in his day. He feels that most North Americans would certainly benefit by spending a part of each day without footwear. Shoes naturally protect feet from accidental injury, but poorly fitted or poorly designed shoes often guarantee nothing more than a trip to the hospital.

After working in India for many years, Dr. Brand realized, to his amazement, that the vast majority of broken ankles and foot problems he had treated were among people who wore shoes. He decided to set up an experiment to determine people's sensitivity in detecting just when their ankles were being twisted.

He built a tilting platform in his office and discovered that people standing bare-footed on the platform could detect even the slightest tilt very rapidly, whereas those who wore shoes took much longer to react.

Shoes decrease the foot's sensitivity and mobility; this decrease in turn affects muscle strength and control in the foot. Dr. Brand also reported that people with naked feet seem to suffer much less from bunions, corns, and ingrown toenails. So, for healthier and happier feet, check first to make sure that there's no broken glass or sharp metal around. Then, whenever possible, try walking without your shoes. Your feet will be grateful.

# Japanese Cowboys

**J**apan is a small country with a large population, where every available piece of land must be used for growing food or raising animals. That's why agricultural scientists at the Grassland Research Institute have developed a remarkable experimental farm that's being used to open up the wild grasslands in Japan's high country. On this farm, you won't see anyone working the herds; it's all done automatically. The rays from the rising sun trigger a photo-electric device that opens up the gates of the cattle pens, allowing one hundred cows to saunter out to pasture for a pleasant day of grazing. While they are on the range, television cameras keep watch, enabling a single supervisor in the farm office to keep a careful eye on the animals.

Later in the day, the cattle are called back to their pens by a tape recorder. It plays a song that the cattle have been trained to recognize as a summons to return to the pens. Once the cows have entered the pens, another electronic scanner counts the animals to make sure that no one is missing, and the cows are given a delicious grain feed as a reward for their obedient behaviour.

Life for these Japanese cows does seem sweet. However, although they eat well and get enough exercise, they may well be lonely, for they never get to see the farmer any more.

If you want to keep your husband happy, just hit him over the head regularly with a big, red club. This strange marriage counselling comes from a team of psychologists at the University of Utah. They found out that open disagreement in a marriage is important for the couple's happiness.

The team armed twenty-three married couples with Bataca bats and set them at each other. The bats are specially designed clubs made of foam rubber wrapped in cloth. They hurt about as much as getting whomped with a pillow. Inside the bats are special sensing devices that tell exactly how hard the couples are hitting each other.

After several good whacking sessions, the researchers found, to their surprise, that couples who seemed the happiest hit each other harder and more frequently than couples who were having problems. Researcher David Young says that the team concluded that the happiest marriages are those where aggression can be expressed openly; and the happiest men are the ones whose wives can enthusiastically wallop away their wifely frustrations, without destroying the underlying affection that binds the couple together.

Pow Your Partner

# Baseball Physics

As every baseball fan undoubtedly knows, the knuckle ball is a pitch that can change its direction so much that it tricks a batter into swinging wildly at the ball. To throw a knuckle ball, the pitcher holds the ball with his fingernails or with the first joints of his fingers so that when he fires it, the ball spins very slowly, or not at all. No one really knew why the knuckle ball worked so well, until two researchers at Tulane University in New Orleans decided to take up baseball in a wind tunnel.

They discovered that aerodynamic forces can make a slowly spinning ball change direction more than a foot as it travels between the pitcher and the batter. The seams on a rotating baseball create a special air pattern around the ball, so that the flow of air is uneven. It's this unevenness that makes the ball move around.

Some pitchers think that a knuckle ball should be thrown without any spin at all, but scientific wind-tunnel evidence shows that it's really the slow spin that makes the knuckle ball so unpredictable. In fact, for the greatest unpredictability, the ball should make a quarter-turn between the pitcher's mound and home plate. And it doesn't seem to matter very much how fast the ball is thrown.

Everyone knows a wax candle is soft and easily crushed. Yet it's possible to fire a candle into a one-inch wooden board at a speed of over a thousand miles per hour, without damaging the candle.

Not only is it unharmed, but it also makes a sharp clean hole right through the board. It's not magic, it's only science.

Researchers in Scotland have taken this incredible scientific phenomenon and used it to develop the world's first supersonic seeder, a gun that shoots seeds into the ground faster than the speed of sound. The gun cuts down seeding time dramatically and, like the candle gun, it plants the delicate seeds without harming them in the slightest way.

The speed of the seed gun creates a shock wave in front of the seed and forms an impenetrable shield of air that cuts a hole in the ground and protects the seed while it's being planted. The wonder gun even allows farmers to resow their fields while the previous crop is still standing.

# Supersonic Seeder

# Bobbing for Energy

Every day, the sea pounds the coast of Britain with a never-ending display of power. Engineers speculate that if a stretch of coastline six hundred miles long could be used to channel wave-power into electricity, one-half of Britain's energy needs could be fulfilled.

Mechanical engineer Stephen Salter of the University of Edinburgh has come up with an experimental device that may turn this dream into a reality. The new device works like a duck bobbing up and down in the water. Shaped like a bulbous triangle, this gigantic bobbing duck moves up and down as the waves come in and hit it. The energy-conversion device sits partly submerged, and every time a large wave hits it, the force of rushing water turns a pump inside it. The turning pump drives a turbine and electricity is produced.

Long rows or booms of these bobbing ducks could be connected together and aimed in the direction of the prevailing wind. In laboratory testing conducted by Britain's Central Electricity Generating Board, researchers discovered that the system is remarkably efficient in converting wave-power into energy. And although we're still a long way from actually heating our tea with the power of the sea, Dr. Salter is working on the first full-scale model, which he hopes will be installed off the coast of Scotland in the very near future.

Under normal circumstances, baby chicks take twenty-one days to hatch. But Nature is fickle and sometimes a bit late. In industry, with enormous production pressures, it's not always possible to wait. Hatchery trays containing chicks are pulled out of the incubator at exactly twenty-one days; any eggs not hatched are simply thrown away.

While trying to find a way to persuade Nature to be punctual, egg researchers discovered an amazing fact: unhatched chicks give off a series of complicated noises, signalling that the birth process is about to begin. The scientists designed special microphones and attached to the eggs a series of electrodes, which monitored these sounds together with the embryos' heartbeats, movement, and breathing. Just before hatching, each embryo started to give off tiny, metallic clicks, which were synchronized with each breath the embryo took. The closer the chick came to hatching, the more urgent the clicks became.

Taking an egg in which the embryo was giving off slow clicks, the scientists played it a tape recording of faster clicks. To their amazement, the slow chick accelerated its movements and hatched more quickly than it would have otherwise.

The team decided that if incubated eggs touched each other, the clicks could be transmitted from egg to egg through the shell. All the incubating chicks might respond and hatch at the same time, the faster ones leading the slower ones. In tests so far, this simple idea has cut down waste by as much as 40 per cent, thanks to the discovery that little chicks who click together, hatch in a batch.

# Eggsploration

If you're a waiter or waitress and want to increase your tips, psychologists at Ohio State University have a magic formula: try to serve those tables where people are eating alone. In a recent experiment conducted at a Columbus, Ohio, steak house, a team of researchers observed that people eating alone were big tippers. These people gave an average of 19 per cent of their total bill, while groups of four to six never left more than an average of 13.5 per cent.

The psychologists explain that when there are several people on a check, no one feels a personal responsibility for the tip. But if the waitress provides separate checks, each person feels singled out and is more likely to tip generously. So, if you're a waiter and find yourself serving a table with a party of six, try to write six individual checks. You just might increase your income.

# Happiness is a Separate Check

# Rocket Lightning Thread

Ever since the day when the first humans were startled by an ominous flash of lightning and the terrifying crash of thunder, we have trembled at the awesome forces of Nature. A bolt of lightning can be a frightening thing, because there seems to be no way of controlling when and where it will strike.

In order to try to make lightning more manageable, a team of physicists from Electricité de France has built an experimental lightning-research station near Saint Privat d'Allier. There, they can direct lightning to a chosen spot and can even cause it to strike in the clouds during a storm, instead of flashing on the ground.

When storm clouds appear on the horizon, special instruments record the electrical field in the cloud and on the ground. When conditions are right, a special rocket is launched at high speed toward the area of high electrical activity in the storm cloud. Attached to the end of the rocket is a fine metal thread that will guide the lightning along its path. Scientists are able to analyse just what happens when the lightning flashes by using electronic instruments protected in a special chamber inside the rocket.

By having the lightning strike the metal thread in the sky rather than something on the ground, French scientists have already induced fifty flashes of lightning, and researchers are hopeful that if the continuing experimentation proves successful, one day, science may be able to control just when and where dangerous lightning bolts will strike.

One of the most serious possible side effects of long periods in a hospital bed is something doctors call "thrombosis", the formation of clots in the blood. These clots can sometimes form when people aren't moving around and normal circulation in the legs slows down. When we walk, the contraction in the calf muscles of our legs plays a major role in helping the blood circulate freely.

Medical science's most recent weapon against thrombosis in the bedridden patient is a pair of special boots that were recently developed in a London hospital. They're placed on the legs during the long periods when the calf muscles can't be exercised normally. The boots work on a massage principle: they are alternately inflated with air for one minute each. As the air goes in and out, the boots provide a gentle massaging action that dramatically improves sluggish circulation throughout the body.

The new boots also have an unexpected side effect: the patients who wear them seem to develop a high concentration of a certain enzyme that stops blood from clotting. Researchers are not sure if it's the massaging action that stimulates the production of this enzyme. They do know there's been a dramatic decrease in blood clots after surgery from patients wearing the new therapeutic footwear. And, as an added bonus, the air-boots seem to help reduce the pain for patients suffering with chronic arthritis.

**Air-Boot Massage**

# Panhandling Pointers

If you're looking for a new career that demands no retraining, lets you set your own hours, and allows you to be your own boss, consider the ancient profession of panhandling. Just walk down the street and hold out your hat. It might become filled with money. A University of Washington research team, headed by psychologist Joan S. Lockard, has come up with a manual of hints that could help you on your way to a successful career as a professional panhandler.

For one thing, you score better if you approach someone of the opposite sex, and someone who is alone. Families and busy groups seem better able to resist the impulse to give, whereas the person walking alone has trouble saying "No". For another thing, there's a right and a wrong way to approach a prospective benefactor. You get the best results if you are sad and submissive, rather than cheerful and demanding.

Tests showed that the ideal panhandling situation is for a single, pathetic female to approach a solitary male when he's eating. Here, primeval history takes a hand. Since the days of the cave man, the male has used food as a mating lure with unfamiliar females. Somehow, he still can't resist the urge.

Undertaken in the right manner, panhandling can be very successful. More than 34 per cent of the people approached generally give something, and that's better than many small businesses do these days.

Plants, like people, have their problems, too. Although they don't have to worry about unpaid bills or about trouble at the office, they do suffer from air pollution, overwatering, and the trauma of being transplanted from one pot to the other. This stressful existence takes a lot out of a plant. Unlike humans, however, they can't tell anyone about it, and if stress goes on too long, the plants may die.

To help plants survive, Dr. Robert O. Linderman of the Ornamental Plant Research Laboratory in Corvallis, Oregon, has found a way to let plants tell their owners about their stressful, chaotic lives. He discovered that plants undergoing certain kinds of stress release an ethylene gas through their pores. By using a special device known as a "gas chromatograph", researchers were able to measure the amount of ethylene that the experimental plants were giving off. Then they could tell exactly when the plants were in trouble.

Keeping a close watch on their instruments, the scientists were able to spot a nervous plant at the very first stages of difficulty, and could solve the problem in no time at all. Dr. Linderman says that this process is still costly and experimental, but perhaps one day it may be available for home use, so that a plant's cry for help can at last be heard.

Nervous Plants

The Soviet Union is having a population problem: not one musk ox has been born there in twenty thousand years. During the last ice age, the Soviet musk ox, that huge shaggy beast that looks like a great hairy bison, was wiped out. But musk oxen of the Canadian Arctic have survived until today.

In order to return the musk ox to its ancestral home, Dr. V.A. Zabrodin and an international team of wildlife specialists airlifted musk oxen from the Canadian Arctic to the frozen tundra of the Soviet Union. In order to move them safely, the scientists used a specially designed, comfort-controlled jet that kept the temperature below zero throughout the trip. The musk oxen were also treated to first-class service, with lots of food and all the comforts of home.

After landing in Moscow, the new Russian herd was immediately taken to Lake Taimyr in Eastern Siberia. Researchers from the International Wildlife Team say that all the musk oxen have adapted well to their new home, and the scientists are anticipating a happy event — news of the first Russian-born musk ox in twenty thousand years.

Musk Ox Airlift

89

It's often been said that one of the most useful things ever invented was the wheel. Wheels changed history. They gave us the industrial revolution, machinery, watches, and vehicles that move and carry things—like the wheelbarrow, for instance. But, like everything else in the world, good things come and go. Regretfully, researchers in Britain announced that the wheelbarrow has finally gone the way of the dinosaur. But how are we going to carry things around without a wheelbarrow?

It's easy. Just replace the wheel with an all-purpose plastic ball, and you've got a new helper that can do some rather remarkable tricks. It can move over muck and mire that would wedge even the most hardy wheel. On the roughest ground, the ballbarrow spreads its weight so evenly that all the jogs and bumps are passed over as easily as silk. And the amazing ballbarrow is practically indestructible. If you get a puncture, all you do is heat the plastic, smooth over the hole with a handy nail, and the ball is resealed. With a

little air inflation, it's ready to roll again.

Best of all, the ballbarrow is fun. Since all work and no play makes barrow pushers dull people, once they're tired of moving the barrow around, all they have to do is give a quick snap to release the ball from its mount, and the versatile ball becomes an instant toy for a bit of football fun at the end of a long workday.

# Bouncing Ballbarrow

# U.S. Nasal Academy

When environmental officials in the San Francisco Bay area receive complaints about foul smells coming from certain areas of the city, a team of dedicated environmental investigators springs into action with the latest devices to measure and evaluate the chemical content of the air. If the smelly polluter happens to be an industry or factory, the investigators are so eager to catch the culprit that they crawl up the sides of smokestacks to collect direct samples of the pollution. Samples are taken back to the laboratory, where they're put under the scrutiny of the most sophisticated device in the world for detecting foul smells: the human nose.

It seems that smell researchers have not been able to create a scientific instrument to compare with the efficiency of the human nose in detecting bad smells. In fact, the nose does such a good job in detecting odours that environment officials in San Francisco decided to set up a panel of impartial noses to decide whether or not a sample of air smells foul. When the environmental agency receives a complaint about a particular odour, the panel of sniffers goes into action. If two of the three noses on the panel correctly identify the samples of pollution, the complaint is considered justified and the violator is given a heavy fine for befouling the environment.

With this panel of dedicated noses hard at work, it shouldn't be long before residents of San Francisco can step outside and be sure they'll get a clean breath of fresh air.

# Operating Bag

Surgery saves countless victims of accident and disease. Despite modern sterilization techniques, however, some lives are still lost because of infection that sets in after the operation. To combat this infection, British surgeons are using a new sterile operating device. It is basically a huge plastic bag inflated with germ-free air. When the pressure is quite high, a nurse breaks the main seal into a simple air lock, providing an area with a constant flow of sterilized air as an extra barrier against invading germs.

Through the air lock, the nurse hands into the bag everything that will be needed for the operation – instruments, sponges, and a pair of sterilized gloves for each member of the operating team. The plastic bag also has built-in arms, each fitted with its own glove.

The device becomes, in effect, a miniature operating theatre.

Instead of going inside the bag, as might be expected, the patient is slipped underneath it. At the bottom of the bag is a square of adhesive that is stuck to the patient over the exact spot where surgery is necessary. By thrusting his hands into the arms of the bag, the surgeon can work on the patient inside a completely sterile atmosphere. From the moment the first incision is made, the inside of the patient's body is exposed to sterile air only, thereby eliminating the risk of infection.

British surgeons report that the marvellous new plastic operating room has been tested in a number of hospitals, and that post-operative infection has been cut almost to zero.

**W**hat's related to the hollyhock and makes newsprint, salad oil, margarine, and animal feed? It's a short, multipurpose tree grown in Australia called the "kenaf", which may revolutionize the forestry industry in the southwest Pacific. Dr. Ian Wood, an agricultural researcher at the Kimberly Research Station, has found the kenaf to be remarkably versatile. A plant that grows to a height of thirteen feet, it has stems that contain long cellulose fibres like those used to make wrapping paper and newsprint.

The seeds of the kenaf contain oils that can be used in salad dressing, cooking oil, and margarine, and after the oil has been removed from the seeds, the remaining pulp contains about 35 per cent protein and can be used as a nutritious supplement for various animal feeds.

Whereas trees used in the manufacture of newsprint usually take ten to twenty years before they can be harvested, kenaf plants mature in only two months, and two good crops can be harvested every season. Although it will be a long time before other trees will be obsolete, the remarkable kenaf tree may give them a good run for their money.

When an oil tanker runs aground and the black crude oil starts gushing out of its holds into the water, an ecological catastrophe is well on the way. As the poisonous oil slick spreads, it smothers, burns, and kills everything in its path. To combat this destruction, scientists from General Electric have discovered a radically new technique for fighting oil spills.

Cellular biologist Ananda M. Chakrabarty has developed a type of bacteria that can actually eat and digest crude oil faster and far more efficiently than anything now available. Moreover, when the little bacteria have finished digesting the oil, they leave behind useful products such as water and carbon dioxide, which can be used by plants.

The oil-guzzling bacteria are easy to breed, and a small colony of the little creatures can produce millions of children and grandchildren in a very short period of time. If all goes well in laboratory and environmental testing, this hungry little superbug will be munching on oil spills to its heart's content, and we'll have another natural tool to help fight the devastating effects of oil pollution.

# Oil Superbug

**E**very year, British farmers lose two million pounds of fruit because of a rather innocent-sounding disease called "silver leaf". The disease is anything but innocent. It strikes quickly and strips away the surface of leaves, making them reflect light so that they look silver-coloured. In time, the leaves can no longer absorb food and the tree must be burned before the fungus spreads.

# Fighting Fungi

Instead of resorting to artificial chemicals, scientists in Britain decided to wage plant warfare by using a special fungus that is harmless to the trees but attacks the spread of silver leaf. Wooden bullets were saturated with the harmless fungus. Then a researcher loaded the bullets into a specially designed gun and fired them into the heart of an infected tree, right through the trunk. Once the bullet was lodged firmly in the tree, the fungus in the bullets moved out to penetrate the tree and kill the disease, before the disease could kill the tree. Researchers report that their fungus champion has been winning every fight so far. This successful experiment is only the first round in a new approach to fighting silver leaf – an approach based on the use of a little help from Nature, instead of dangerous man-made chemicals.

# Sea Snake Surprise

If you're a skin diver looking for ocean treasure, or a scientist diving beneath the sea for knowledge, it's not always easy to keep killer sharks away. Dr. Walt Stark, an underwater researcher, came up with an unusual solution: pretend you're a sea snake.

The poisonous, zebra-striped sea snake is never attacked by sharks. Neither is the pilot fish, which has a similar kind of marking. For centuries, villagers who lived on the Pacific islands covered their bodies with alternating bands of charcoal and white clay to celebrate the sea snake in a ritual dance, because the snake keeps sharks away from their fishing nets.

While Dr. Stark was conducting a research program near the Banks Islands in the South Pacific, he found out about the sea snake and decided to cover his diving suit in black and white stripes.to see what would happen. The scientist admits that at first he was a little scared; but the black and white suit worked so well in confusing the sharks that they not only kept their distance, but also usually cleared the area completely.

Later, he and four other divers went down together into the shark-filled waters. The divers wearing conventional diving suits were quickly surrounded by sharks, but the divers wearing Dr. Stark's striped suits completely fooled the vicious predators. The sharks would come within ten feet, take one look, then clear out in a flash. Even the most aggressive and sharp-eyed sharks become highly disoriented by the new diving suit, which may become the diver's best protective colouring while exploring shark-infested seas.

**M**eat is one of the best sources of protein. But in many parts of the world, it's very difficult to raise a herd of high-quality cattle. One of the answers science has found in its quest for ways to improve the world's beef supply is to implant fertilized eggs from top-quality cows into cows of lower quality. To accomplish this, the eggs are usually frozen after being removed from the original mother; but often the eggs do not survive shipment over long distances.

Now, English zoologists at the Animal Research Centre in Cambridge have come up with one of the world's most unusual shipping and storage containers: live rabbits. By means of a simple and safe operation, veterinarians remove newly fertilized eggs from high-quality cows and implant them in a rabbit. Each rabbit, like a living incubator with its cargo of cow eggs, is then shipped to its destination. When it arrives, the eggs are taken from the rabbit and each egg is placed in a low-grade cow, which will bring to life a strong, healthy calf. The rabbit, its mission completed, can hop away happily to more rabbit-like pursuits.

The rabbit containers have been so successful that zoologists are looking into other areas where the technique can be applied. One day, rabbit astronauts may even carry the seeds for new animal colonies into the far reaches of outer space.

From the Soviet Union comes news of another remarkable development pioneered by cosmonauts during space exploration. One of the spin-offs of Soviet space research has been the development of a highly sophisticated monitoring system, where all the vital functions of a person can be carefully watched on a continuous basis. Researchers in the Biotelemetrics Research Laboratory of the Kislovodsk Sanatorium have applied the technique to several of their heart patients, who were so ill that they were afraid to climb a set of stairs.

The new monitoring system allows these patients to do many of the active things that they once thought were impossible. They can take long walks in the mountain air or ice skate on a cold winter's day, secure in the knowledge that a team of doctors is watching and following every step. The patient carries a backpack that looks like a portable radio with a long antenna. This device sends all his vital signs back to a control panel at the laboratory. If the patient is engaged in an activity that seems too strenuous for his condition, a little bell rings, alerting the patient to stop what he's doing immediately and report to the hospital.

Dr. L. I. Tatarenko, head of the biotelemetric laboratory, reports that although the new method needs refining, early testing has proven remarkably successful. He soon hopes to employ computers to expand remote-control observations, so that one day all twelve thousand sanatorium patients can be monitored, enabling them to lead more normal lives.

# Heart Monitors

Ordinary tap water can now be changed in a jiffy into a quivering, shaking blob: instant jellied water. A team of British researchers has added a pinch of laponite and made unspillable water. As long as no steady pressure is directed at the water, it remains in jelly form. When the water starts pouring again, the pressure makes it become liquid instantly.

What seems like a magician's trick is simply another one of the physical wonders of the world. The molecules in laponite have an almost magnetic attraction for each other and, in an undisturbed state, they rush toward each other and hold on tightly in a jumbled mass, turning liquid into jelly.

Jellied water could be a very important aid in fighting fires: think of water that stays where you put it once it leaves the hose – water that doesn't evaporate or run away. It's an instant fire extinguisher, since walls covered with the stuff just won't burn.

In hospitals, jelly water could save many hours of work for nurses, if it were used as a mattress for severely ill or injured patients who couldn't move themselves. Instead of having nurses move the patients to prevent bed sores, jellied water would mould evenly around the contours of a patient's body, allowing him to rest comfortably without developing pressure sores.

And for those people with fears of burst waterbeds, solid water may be just the answer they've been looking for.

# Nondrip Development

For years, frustrated Spanish farmers have observed that their cows will only eat grass that is standing straight up. The cows are so lazy that they hate eating grass that has been trampled or flattened down. Since farmers couldn't get the cows to bend over, scientists decided to do something to the grass.

At the Zoological Institute in Cordoba, researchers have come up with an inventive solution. After years of experimentation, they've finally created a special strain of grass that springs right back up after the cattle hooves have flattened it. Thousands of acres of the experimental grass have been planted. And the lazy cows are now eating so well that their gain in weight has been as much as 10 per cent.

# Springy Spanish Grass

In modern homes, it seems that everyone wants to listen to something different—television, the stereo, or the radio. To prevent our lives from tumbling into sonic chaos, German scientists have developed a revolutionary concept in sound transmission that involves sending sound via waves of infra-red light. The new system, designed at the Sennheiser Company, allows people to hear sound through battery-powered cordless headphones. They can be tuned into any sound source that is sending out special infra-red signals. The infra-red transmitting device can be plugged into any earphone jack on a television, stereo, or radio. This cuts off the sound and translates it into infra-red signals. The signals literally flood a room, so there's no need to sit near the source, or even to face it.

In the home, with all the family together in one room, each person can be tuned into something different. At the same time, in the middle of all this, someone else can sit quietly reading a book, and not hear a sound.

Specialists have applied this concept to the teaching of deaf children. One of the frustrations in teaching these children is having to keep active youngsters seated near a sound source in order to communicate with them. Now, with the new cordless headsets, the children can wander around the room, playing or working, and still remain in constant touch with the teacher.

# Cordless Headphones

# Mosquito Drowning

After years of battling mosquitos, scientists at the Naval Research Laboratory in Washington, DC, have come up with a control method that's so safe and simple that they are wondering why no one thought of it before. Instead of sterilizing, spraying, and generally cursing the little pests, scientists are simply drowning them.

When mosquito eggs become larvae, they survive by clinging to the surface of the water. This is made possible by a special property of water called "surface tension". In the new control method, the researchers apply a small amount of a special liquid, which quickly spreads over the surface of the water like a film. The film breaks up the surface tension so completely that the mosquito larvae have nothing to cling to. They sink to the bottom and drown.

The new method is a big improvement over older mosquito-control methods, because it doesn't use harmful pesticides that pollute the environment and endanger other species. And because it's an organic liquid, it does not starve the marine life of oxygen. Dr. William D. Garrett, the discoverer of the technique, says that the method is so safe it can be used on large open bodies of water, such as irrigation projects and reservoirs. It's not only completely nontoxic to humans; recent field tests proved it to be 100 per cent successful.

only at night, the device consists of a small radio receiver about the size of a silver dollar. It's implanted in the back under the skin, just below the rib cage, and every ten seconds tiny electronic probes stimulate muscles that pull on the spine.

Installing the device is a simple operation and the patients are up and around the same day. They feel absolutely no discomfort and can carry on with almost any activity. As long as the child's bones are still growing, the once-crippling handicap can be corrected with this remarkable new muscle pacemaker, and complete recovery usually occurs within a couple of years.

Until recently, there were two ways to treat children with scoliosis, or curvature of the spine. The young patient most frequently was placed in a brace "cage" that was worn for the remaining growing period. The second method was a painful operation that straightened and partly immobilized the spine with a steel rod, so that many types of movement were no longer possible.

Thanks to a new technique developed by Dr. Walter Bobechko, an orthopedic surgeon, and Dr. Morley Herbert, a biophysicist, at the Hospital for Sick Children in Toronto, scoliosis victims can now be treated to correct their spinal deformities without pain, or major surgery. And it all happens while they're asleep.

The revolutionary method uses a modified heart pacemaker that stimulates the back muscles to make the body itself correct the curvature. Used

# Scoliosis Pacemaker

Body odour is looked upon in our society as somewhat offensive. Most people put on deodorant every morning in order to cover up bad smells. But the odour is actually caused by bacteria, and scientists think that they have now found a way to attack the bacteria itself.

In an experimental project, researchers at the United States Department of Agriculture discovered a way to make fabrics with built-in sterilizing substances that kill bacteria found on the body. These special chemical compounds adhere so well to certain types of cloth that the sterilizing technique can be used in many remarkable ways. Researchers believe that hospital sheets and towels, for example, could be treated with this slow-release chemical to cut down the spread of germs and infection. Scientists also believe that they can easily produce a whole range of everyday household items – towels that resist mildew, socks that fight athletes' foot, and clothes that release their own bleaches and stain-removers in the wash.

It seems that the best material for absorbing the sterilizing substance is cotton. The treated cloth has been found to be completely free of bacteria, even after fifty experimental launderings in the laboratory washing machine. However, Dr. Tyron Vigo, head of the research project, says that scientists must prove that there are no toxic side effects before the remarkable self-sterilizing items can appear on department-store shelves and make life a whole lot cleaner and smell-free.

In the past few years, with all the teenagers wearing bluejeans and long hair, some people have been complaining that they simply can't tell the boys from the girls. A group of psychologists in Knoxville, Tennessee, has come up with a foolproof way of telling the difference: just watch how the kids carry their books.

It seems that almost all high-school-age boys carry their books by their sides, with arms straight and fingers gripping the books tightly. Eight out of ten girls, on the other hand, rest the lower edges of their books on their hipbones or clutch the books tightly to their chests. The different carrying methods might be explained by obvious differences in the size, strength, and body shapes of boys and girls.

# Girls Boys and Books

Even in early primary classes, however, girls start carrying their books differently. Since height, weight, and body shape are quite similar in boys and girls until about age twelve, the different book-carrying postures can't be caused by anatomy alone. After much careful research, no one is quite sure exactly why the sexes favour their particular carrying methods, although one possible explanation is evolution. The female position is very similar to that used for carrying babies or young children, while the arms-at-the-side, masculine style is more convenient for carrying weapons or tools. Whatever the reason, if you're still having trouble sorting out the sexes on their way to school, just take a closer look at the way they're carrying their books.

If something far away looks blurred and out of focus, but you can see very clearly things that are close to you, you're nearsighted. This common vision problem can be corrected by eyeglasses, but they don't cure the problem.

Now, two American doctors, ophthalmologists Charles May and Stuart Grant, think that they've found a way to cure the widespread vision defect. The new technique, called "orthokeratology", fits the eye with a series of contact lenses that actually cause the eye to reshape itself, in the same way that braces straighten out crooked teeth.

The eye doctor fits a patient with a tight but comfortable contact lens that gently squeezes the cornea, the front part of the eyeball that affects the images we see. As a result, the cornea gradually begins to flatten, so that in two to four weeks the patient's sight has improved slightly. When this occurs, a new pair of contact lenses is fitted to the changing cornea, and with more squeezing, more gradual flattening takes place.

The lenses are changed nearly every six weeks, until the patient has 20/20 vision, or until there's no further improvement in the patient's eyes. This treatment has been permanently successful in 80 per cent of the cases tried so far, bringing people's fuzzy worlds into focus without the aid of glasses for the first time.

# Sight Straighteners

One of the biggest headaches that oil-importing countries are stuck with is the constant problem of spills from tankers carrying oil. Until recently, the most common way to deal with the problem was to spray thousands of gallons of detergent onto the oil. But since each gallon of slick also needed a gallon of costly detergent to dissolve it, this procedure was expensive, to say the least.

Now, treating oil spills may become a routine matter, thanks to a little rig that skims oil off water the way a farmer takes cream off the top of milk. In working out the rig's design, researchers in Britain made use of two natural properties of oil: the fact that it floats on water because it's lighter, and the fact that it clings to almost any surface.

As the new skimmer moves along the oil-drenched surface, a set of cheap plastic discs, propelled by compressed air, dips in and out of the water. The oil clings naturally to the discs, much as it does to a hand that's dipped into a container of oil. The skimmer then uses a set of squeegees to scrape the oil off the discs and to feed the oil into a central area, which will be pumped out later.

The mini-skimmer can be operated by two people and can collect ten tons of oil in one hour. Its larger brother, the maxi-skimmer, can recover oil at the rate of one hundred tons an hour. It's not only the cheapest method of cleaning up spills, it also saves all that spilled oil; once the oil has been skimmed off, it can be sent to a refinery and recycled for later use.

**Oil Skimmer**

When a baby is born prematurely, it loses time that is normally spent in the comfort and safety of the mother's womb. This shock of being born too early can sometimes have serious effects on the child as it grows and develops. So, in order to keep the tiny infant in a more womb-like environment, Dr. Kathryn Barnard of the University of Washington's Child Development Centre has developed a mechanical mother, which rocks the premature baby back and forth while providing the continuous sounds of maternal heartbeats through a speaker.

The mechanical mother is really a special incubator that copies the sounds and motions that a baby might experience in the womb. Tests on fifteen babies born one to two months prematurely showed that, in the new device, they slept more quietly and gained more weight than did babies who were placed in normal incubators.

In a follow-up study a year later, these same babies seemed to be easier to care for, and the mothers reported that there were no problems in their early growth and development.

Although there's still no substitute for development in the protected warmth of a mother's womb, doctors can now give premature babies a better chance in life by providing a world that's just a little closer to the one that they lost.

## Mechanical Mother

# Staring Kids

If you want to have terrific children, make sure that they wander around and stare a lot.

A new study by psychological researchers at Harvard University shows that the brightest and happiest children all seem to be doing the same things when they are very young. They listen to conversation even before they can understand what it's all about. They are allowed to roam freely around the home with few restrictions. And they spend a lot of time staring.

Strange as it may seem, the researchers discovered that the more a child stares at his surroundings, the more likely it is that he will be well adjusted when he grows up. Staring seems to be the single most common experience of young children, and the ones who turn out to be the most healthy adults psychologically are the ones who spent more than 20 per cent of their time just staring when they were kids.

Coyotes and wolves have come to think of sheep as a really good meal. Farmers try almost everything to stop these killers from getting at their flocks, but so far nothing has been very effective. Now, a team of research ecologists from Eastern Washington State College has come up with a new and humane way to save the sheep from their attackers.

In careful experiments with the dangerous animals, the researchers discovered that a special salty chemical placed inside a piece of meat could make the coyotes very sick, but it wouldn't do any permanent harm. After eating the experimental food just once in laboratory tests, the coyotes became so nauseous that they couldn't eat anything and wouldn't even look at a sheep when it was placed right in front of them.

After slaughtering a sheep and lacing its flesh with the salty substance, the researchers left the dead sheep as bait on the outskirts of a farm. At night, the coyotes came to feed on the sheep and, before they knew it, they were sick to their stomachs. As a matter of fact, they felt so awful that they couldn't even stand the smell and taste of sheep any longer. By scattering the salty experimental bait around the edges of a sheep farm, the research team can reduce by 50 per cent the number of sheep that are killed.

If you happen to be worried, anxious, and jumpy, help is closer than you'd ever think possible. It's right at your feet. Dr. Richard Driscoll, a psychologist at Eastern State Psychiatric Hospital in Tennessee, recently conducted a study with a group of men and women who all suffered from the same problem: they became extremely nervous before exams. In order to help these students, Dr. Driscoll decided to try an experiment that tested various techniques for reducing exam-time anxiety.

He divided the students into four groups and gave them each separate tasks. The first group was told to get out and jog before an exam. The second group was asked to sit back and imagine a pleasant situation.

The third group was told to jog but, in addition, to think of pleasant thoughts while they were out running around the track. The fourth group had the worst time of all; they were asked to do nothing – just sit there and worry.

Each student's level of anxiety was tested and rated before and after the exams. When the results were in, the researchers discovered that the group of students who were out jogging and thinking of pleasant things showed the greatest drop in anxiety. As well, they scored the best marks on the exams. As simple as it sounds, Dr. Driscoll believes that running around and thinking happy thoughts are truly effective ways to cope with the pressures of day-to-day life. So the next time you've got the jitters, start thinking happy thoughts. Then put on your sneakers and just trot your troubles away.

Jumpy Joggers

# Burns Hoverbed

When a person is burned very badly, doctors are faced with a twofold treatment problem: easing the extreme pain and preventing infection. It seems that human skin acts like a bag to hold the liquids that defend the body from bacteria. When the skin is broken or destroyed, as it is in a severe burn, the liquids are lost and the patient is wide open to possible infection.

In the past, victims of burns were kept totally isolated for months, because any contact with the outside world could cause a dangerous infection. But such extreme measures may no longer be necessary. British medical researchers in a London hospital have come up with a revolutionary bed that may completely change the traditional way of treating serious burns.

The remarkable bed actually floats the patient on a soft cushion of air. Since nothing touches the patient's highly sensitive skin, there's much less pain. The air released from a canopy above the bed surrounds the person so completely that it also acts like a protective shield, keeping bacteria and infection away from the delicate skin while it heals. The air is sterile, humidified, and heated to the exact body temperature.

This constant flow of air is necessary to help the body form a protective, scab-like covering, which is nature's dressing for wounds. With the new system, the protective scab forms within thirty-six to forty-eight hours, much more quickly than ever before. Doctors report that victims of burns can now be treated in greater safety, without the necessity of isolating them from the comfort of friends during the long recovery period.

Traffic-safety engineers are looking for ways to help bus drivers fight off boredom, frustration, and aggression. These feelings, especially boredom, are often the cause of mistakes and errors in judgement that lead to traffic accidents.

In the air, many of the boring details of flying an airplane are turned over to an automatic co-pilot; so why not do the same on land? British scientists at the Road Research Laboratory near London have designed a remarkable bus that seems to think for itself. There is no driver. The automatic bus steers itself by following a special cable buried in the road. Two shields on the front of the bus act as guides and keep the bus centred in its lane.

To make this system workable on a large scale would require solution of the incredible engineering problems involved in burying the necessary miles of cable over the entire bus route. But the gain in traffic safety might be worth it. The driverless bus may be the first step toward automated travel, where people can simply chart a course, then sit back and enjoy the ride; the driver will never become tired, bored, or frustrated, and errors in driving judgement will be kept to a minimum.

Driverless Bus

Pocketscope

**H**elicopter pilots who fly rescue missions at night sometimes find their work extremely dangerous, because it's so hard to see just what's out there in the darkness. With the help of new electronic "goggles", however, a pilot can see so well that he'll be able to fly through rugged canyons at night, in perfect safety, with only the light of the stars to guide his way. The new device, called a "pocketscope", was developed by the United States Army's Night Vision Laboratory.

The pocketscope weighs only eleven ounces and measures seven inches in length. It's equipped with a miniature television system that amplifies the night light and transmits a much brighter picture through the camera lens to the retina of the eye.

In addition to night-flying pilots, some children and young adults who have an hereditary eye disease called "night-vision blindness" also have trouble seeing at night. After fifteen years of research, scientists at ITT's Electro-Optical Laboratory have adapted the army device for medical purposes. Research physicians at the Massachusetts Eye and Ear Infirmary in Boston say that there is presently no way to cure night-vision blindness. But the pocketscope is being used by doctors in an experimental program, to provide years of useful vision while the search for a cure goes on.

If you've ever had a toothache or found that your mouth was full of cavities, there's a new idea from England that promises to solve your dental problems. According to dental researcher R.V. Tait, we've got too many teeth. He suggests that if we pull some of them out, our dental problems will be reduced.

Since our present-day diet is vastly different from the gritty, fibrous food our ancient ancestors had to chew, Dr. Tait feels that we no longer need thirty-two teeth. Our overpopulated mouths can be modernized by gradually reducing the number of teeth either to twenty or twenty-four during early childhood.

With the mouth less crowded, there will be fewer cavities, no impacted wisdom teeth, and fewer visits to the dentist. But before you get too excited about this wonderful new remedy, don't forget about that initial visit to the dentist — when he pulls out all those extra teeth.

# Pull Out Extra Teeth

# Biting Bossies

In Australia, animal researchers have discovered a new way to tell which cows are earning their keep and which ones are slacking off. They watch to see how fast the cows are biting their food.

A group of Australian scientists in Brisbane, interested in improving milk production, were studying the grazing habits of Jersey cows and found that the average cow grazes from 540 to 720 minutes per day. During this time, she takes thirty-six thousand bites, and with each bite swallows three-tenths of a gram of grass.

After metering thousands of munches in this way, the researchers discovered that if two cows eat the same amount of grass in a given day, the cow that chews the grass faster will produce more milk. Scientists are now advising farmers that when they go to market to buy new cows, they should pay close attention to how fast each cow can eat the grass. The quicker the chomp, the more the milk.

**E**verything is going portable these days. The latest thing on the move is an entire underwater laboratory in a plastic bag. British scientists have started using gigantic plastic bags almost one hundred feet long to enclose the samples, the watery environment, and all the testing equipment needed to study pollution right where it happens – in the middle of the sea.

Divers take the huge plastic bags down into position, where they are filled with twenty-five thousand gallons of sea water and all the inhabitants of such a section of the sea. The living sea community becomes an enclosed laboratory, where scientists can add or subtract chemicals to study plant and animal reactions.

In one test, the British scientists sprayed the underwater lab with copper, a common and much-feared pollutant. They were able to obtain a true picture of the effects of such pollution. Much to their surprise and delight, they found that the copper was not nearly as lethal as they had expected. Since further tests showed that marine life is far more adaptable than had been supposed, the special plastic-bag laboratories have already proven their real worth in understanding sea pollution, and in helping to hasten the day when it can be controlled.

# Baggies Beneath the Sea

# Algae Miners

**A**lgae, a humble, one-celled plant that lives in water, may one day serve people by mining the seas. In laboratory tests, German scientists at the Chemical Institute of the Julich Nuclear Research Plant have discovered a type of algae that actually "eats" uranium.

It is well known that sea water contains many important minerals, but in such minute quantities that it has been impossible to extract them from the sea. Because this newly discovered algae absorbs uranium directly into itself, however, it may be possible one day to release a huge colony of algae into the ocean and, after they have had a good feed, to collect them all back again and just "squeeze" out the uranium. Researchers are now investigating the possibility of using the "algae miners" commercially. If the process is successful, it may lead to extensive mining of other valuable minerals found in the ocean depths.

If you were looking at a flying aircraft with infra-red eyes, you'd spot a strange hurricane following in its path. This invisible turbulence isn't a freak of nature. It's the result of all the currents of air that have been stirred up by the airplane. They actually help keep the plane flying.

If another plane follows too closely, however, and cuts into the swirling trail of air, tragedy could result. When a huge plane comes in for a landing, it brings with itself these swirling currents of air – and potential danger.

To prevent tragic accidents, British research engineers at Heathrow Airport have developed an invisible, infra-red laser device that acts like supersensitive radar. As each plane approaches for landing, the device beams out a laser signal that measures the movement of air following the plane. If the turbulence is too great, controllers can warn other planes to bypass the runway until it's safe to land.

Airport officials believe that the new device will prevent accidents. More than that, it holds promise for new jets, which may be able to control and break up their own turbulence without danger to themselves or to any aircraft behind them.

# Laser Radar

# Canine Contacts

For people who don't like wearing glasses, contact lenses have been a blessing. Now dogs are starting to wear them, too. Dr. Gretchen Schmidt of Michigan State University has discovered a remarkable new use for ordinary soft contact lenses. They are used as see-through bandages for dogs who have serious eye diseases. They remain over the dog's afflicted eyes for about two weeks, allowing the very sensitive eye tissue to heal rapidly, without any pain whatsoever.

The new soft-lens technique is so successful that it actually eliminates the need for surgery, and because the contact lenses are painless, there is no need to use anaesthetics. The new treatment works well on all dogs, but poodles and terriers seem to receive the best fit, since their eyes are about the same size and shape as human eyes.

We know that noise is a nuisance. Recently psychologist Lance Cannon set up an experiment to see if the presence of noise can actually change a person's behaviour. In a residential area of a small town, the researcher came out of a house wearing a cast on his arm, and pretended to struggle with two huge boxes overflowing with books.

The purpose of the experiment was to find out if people walking by on the street would stop to help. When the experiment was carried out on a quiet street, almost all the people who passed by took the time to help the supposedly injured man.

But when the same experiment was carried out with a noisy power lawnmower operating nearby, only 15 per cent of the people bothered to stop.

Dr. Cannon concludes that people go from nice to nasty all because of the noise.

# Noise Makes Nasty

Every minute of the day, whether we're awake or asleep, millions of nerve impulses travel through our bodies at incredible speeds. But if the speed of these nerve impulses slows down, it could mean that something is seriously wrong in the body. Doctors know that if they could easily detect the speed at which the electrical impulses travel, they would have a helpful indicator in determining whether or not someone is sick.

Dr. Percy Hammond of the Warren Spring Laboratory in England has come up with a new device that serves as a nerve speedometer.

Electrodes hooked up to the new machine are placed on the major nerves found in the elbow and the thumb. Then a small, painless electric shock is given through the elbow electrode. This shock stimulates the nerve, which sends a signal down the arm, where it's picked up by a special electronic sensor attached to the thumb. The time it takes the nerve impulse to travel between the elbow and the thumb is automatically calculated and then divided by the distance between these points; the resulting figure is the speed of conduction of the nerve.

Researchers have already started testing the nerve speedometer in a London hospital, and they're confident of every success. Since the new machine is so simple and safe to use, nurses without any special training can test patients as easily as they now take a temperature. When a change in the speed of nerve impulses is detected, doctors will have an invaluable early-warning system, alerting them to look more closely at a patient before he becomes more seriously ill.

Nerve Speedometer

# Index

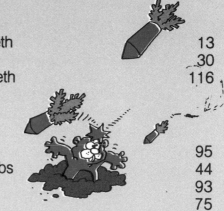

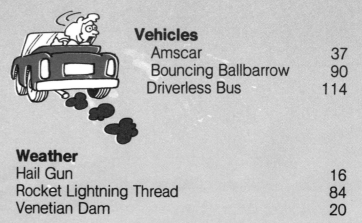

Illustrated by: Roy Condy

Designed by: Galer & MacMillan Communication Inc.

Cover illustrations by: Matti Korhonen

Typesetting by: Accutext Ltd.

Printing and binding by: Webcom Ltd.